THE RHYMING RIVER

III

POETRY BOOKS BY JAMES REEVES

ANTHOLOGIES

Heinemann's Junior Poetry Books:
1 *Yellow Wheels*   2 *Grey Goose and Gander*
3 *Green Broom*   4 *Strawberry Fair*
The Merry-Go-Round (the above four books in one volume)
The Rhyming River: an anthology of poetry for secondary schools
 Book One (illustrated by Peter Dunbar)
 Book Two (illustrated by Jane Paton)
 Book Three (illustrated by Robert Hodgson)
 Book Four (illustrated by Peggy Fortnum)
Orpheus Book I (English poetry for 10–12-year-olds)
Orpheus Book II (English poetry for 13–15-year-olds)
The Poets' World (an anthology of English poetry)
The Speaking Oak (a miscellany of English prose and poetry)
A New Canon of English Poetry with M. Seymour-Smith

POEMS FOR CHILDREN

Hurdy Gurdy
The Wandering Moon
Prefabulous Animiles with Edward Ardizzone

THE POETRY BOOKSHELF SERIES

Selections with introductions and notes
D. H. Lawrence
John Donne
Gerard Manley Hopkins
John Clare
Robert Browning
Samuel Taylor Coleridge
Emily Dickinson
The Modern Poets' World
Jonathan Swift

MISCELLANEOUS

A Short History of English Poetry
Idiom of the People
Understanding Poetry
The Everlasting Circle
Teaching Poetry

THE RHYMING RIVER

BOOK THREE

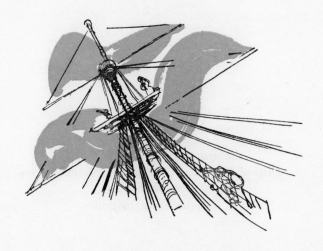

an anthology of verse chosen by
JAMES REEVES

with illustrations by
ROBERT HODGSON
and from contemporary sources

HEINEMANN EDUCATIONAL
BOOKS LTD · LONDON

Heinemann Educational Books Ltd
LONDON MELBOURNE TORONTO
SINGAPORE JOHANNESBURG
HONG KONG NAIROBI
AUCKLAND IBADAN

Published by
Heinemann Educational Books Ltd
48 Charles Street London W1
Printed in Great Britain by
Butler & Tanner Ltd
Frome and London

CONTENTS

I

II

III

IV

V

VI

VII

VIII

I

The Beechwood

When the long, varnished buds of beech
Point out beyond their reach,
And tanned by summer suns
Leaves of black bryony turn bronze,
And gossamer floats bright and wet
From trees that are their own sunset,
Spring, summer, autumn I come here,
And what is there to fear?
And yet I never lose the feeling
That someone close behind is stealing
Or else in front has disappeared;
Though nothing I have seen or heard,
The fear of what I might have met
Makes me still walk beneath those boughs
With cautious step as in a haunted house.

ANDREW YOUNG

Many a Mickle

A little sound—
Only a little, a little—
The breath in a reed,
A trembling fiddle;
The trumpet's ring,
The shuddering drum;
So all the glory, bravery, hush
Of music come.

A little sound—
Only a stir and a sigh
Of each green leaf
Its fluttering neighbour by;
Oak on to oak,
The wide dark forest through—
So o'er the watery wheeling world
The night winds go.

A little sound,
Only a little, a little—
The thin high drone
Of the simmering kettle,
The gathering frost,
The click of needle and thread;
Mother, the fading wall, the dream,
The drowsy bed.

WALTER DE LA MARE

Break of Day

THE lark he rises early,
  And the ploughman goes away
Before it's morning fairly
  At the guessing break of day;
The fields lie in the dawning,
  And the valley's hid in gold,
At the pleasant time of morning
  When the shepherd goes to fold.

The maiden laughs and hollos
  When she sees the feeding cows;
They switch their tails and follow
  When she can't get over sloughs;
I love the gentle dawning,
  And the valleys hid in gold,
At the pleasant time of morning
  When the shepherd goes to fold.

JOHN CLARE

3

Verses from 'The Sluggard'

'Tis the voice of the sluggard; I heard him complain,
'You have wak'd me too soon, I must slumber again.'
As the door on its hinges, so he on his bed,
Turns his sides and his shoulders and his heavy head.

'A little more sleep, and a little more slumber;'
Thus he wastes half his days and his hours without number;
And when he gets up, he sits folding his hands,
Or walks about sauntering, or trifling he stands.

I pass'd by his garden, and saw the wild brier,
The thorn and the thistle grow broader and higher;
The clothes that hang on him are turning to rags;
And his money still wastes, till he starves or he begs.

ISAAC WATTS

Schoolboys in Winter

THE schoolboys still their morning rambles take
To neighbouring village school with playing speed,
Loitering with pastime's leisure till they quake,
Oft looking up the wild-geese droves to heed,
Watching the letters which their journeys make;
Or plucking haws on which the fieldfares feed,
And hips, and sloes; and on each shallow lake
Making glib slides, where they like shadows go
Till some fresh pastimes in their minds awake.
Then off they start anew and hasty blow
Their numbed and clumpsing fingers till they glow;
Then races with their shadows wildly run
That stride huge giants o'er the shining snow
In the pale splendour of the winter sun.

JOHN CLARE

The Drum

I HATE that drum's discordant sound,
Parading round, and round, and round:
To thoughtless youth it pleasure yields,
And lures from cities and from fields,
To sell their liberty for charms
Of tawdry lace, and glittering arms;
And when Ambition's voice commands,
To march, and fight, and fall, in foreign lands.

I hate that drum's discordant sound,
Parading round, and round, and round,
To me it talks of ravaged plains,
And burning towns, and ruined swains,
And mangled limbs, and dying groans,
And widows' tears, and orphans' moans;
And all that Misery's hand bestows,
To fill the catalogue of human woes.

JOHN SCOTT

Summer

WINTER is cold-hearted,
  Spring is yea and nay,
Autumn is a weathercock
  Blown every way:
Summer days for me
When every leaf is on its tree;

When Robin's not a beggar,
  And Jenny Wren's a bride,
And larks hang singing, singing, singing,
  Over the wheat-fields wide,
  And anchored lilies ride,
And the pendulum spider
  Swings from side to side.

And blue-black beetles transact business,
  And gnats fly in a host,
And furry caterpillars hasten
  That no time be lost,
And moths grow fat and thrive,
And ladybirds arrive.

Before green apples blush,
  Before green nuts embrown,
Why, one day in the country
  Is worth a month in town;
  Is worth a day and a year
Of the dusty, musty, lag-last fashion
  That days drone elsewhere.

CHRISTINA ROSSETTI

Sudden Shower

BLACK grows the southern sky, betokening rain,
  And humming hive-bees homeward hurry by:
They feel the change; so let us shun the grain,
  And take the broad road while our feet are dry.
Ay, there some dropples moistened on my face,
  And pattered on my hat—'tis coming nigh!
Let's look about, and find a sheltering place.
  The little things around, like you and I,
Are hurrying through the grass to shun the shower.
  Here stoops an ash-tree—hark! the wind gets high,
But never mind; this ivy for an hour,
  Rain as it may, will keep us dryly here:
That little wren knows well his sheltering bower,
  Nor leaves his dry house though we come so near.

JOHN CLARE

The Start of a Steeplechase

(from *Right Royal*)

THE horses sparred as though drunk with wine,
They bickered and snatched at taking line.

Then a grey-haired man with a hawk-like face
Read from a list each rider's place.
Sitting astride his pommely hack,
He ordered them up or sent them back;
He bade them heed that they jump their nags
Over every jump between the flags.
Here Kubbadar, who was pulling double,
Went sideways, kicking and raising trouble,
Monkery seconded, kicking and biting,
Thunderbolt followed by starting fighting.

The starter eyed them and gave the order
That the three wild horses keep the border,
With men to hold them to keep them quiet.
Boys from the stable stopped their riot.
Out of the line to the edge of the field
The three wild biters and kickers wheeled;
Then the rest edged up and pawed and bickered,
Reached at their reins and snatched and snickered,
Flung white foam as they stamped their hate
Of passionate blood compelled to wait.

Then the starter shouted to Charles, 'Good heaven,
This isn't a circus, you on Seven.'
For Royal squirmed like a box of tricks
And Coranto's rider, the number Six,
Cursed at Charles for a green young fool
Who ought to be at a riding school.
After a minute of swerves and shoving,
A line like a half-moon started moving,
Then Rocket and Soyland leaped to stride,
To be pulled up short and wheeled to side.
Then the trickier riders started thrusting,
Judging the starter's mind too trusting;
But the starter said, 'You know quite clearly
That isn't allowed; though you'd like it dearly.'

Then Cannonade made a sideways bolt
That gave Exception an ugly jolt.
Then the line, re-formed, broke all to pieces.
Then the line re-forms, and the tumult ceases.
Each man sits tense though his racer dances;
In a slow, jerked walk the line advances.

And then in a flash, more felt than seen,
The flag shot down and the course showed green,
And the line surged forwards and all that glory
Of speed was sweeping to make a story.

One second before, Charles Cothill's mind
Had been filled with fear to be left behind,
But now with a rush, as when hounds leave cover,
The line broke up and his fear was over.
A glimmer of bay behind The Ghost
Showed Dear Adonis still at the post.
Out to the left, a joy to his backer,
Kubbadar led the field in a cracker,
The thunder of horses, all fit and foaming,

Made the blood not care whether death were coming.
A glimmer of silks, blue, white, green, red,
Flashed into his eye and went ahead;
Then hoof-casts scattered, then rushing horses
Passed at his side with all their forces.
His blood leapt up but his mind said 'No,
Steady my darling, slow, go slow.
In the first time round this ride's a hunt.'

The Turk's Grave Fence made a line in front.

Long years before, when the race began,
That first of the jumps had maimed a man;
His horse, the Turk, had been killed and buried
There in the ditch by horse-hoofs herried;
And over the poor Turk's bones at pace
Now, every year, there goes the race,

And many a man makes doctor's work
At the thorn-bound ditch that hides the Turk,
And every man as he rides that course
Thinks, there, of the Turk, that good old horse.

The thick thorn-fence stands five feet high,
With a ditch beyond unseen by eye,
Which a horse must guess from his urgent rider
Pressing him there to jump it wider.

And being so near both Stand and Post,
Out of all the jumps men haunt it most,
And there, with the crowd, and the undulled nerves,
The old horse balks and the young horse swerves,
And the good horse falls with the bad on top
And beautiful boldness comes to stop.
Charles saw the rush of the leading black,
And the forehands lift and the men sway back;
He steadied his horse, then with crash and crying,
The top of the Turk's Grave Fence went flying.

Round in a flash, refusing danger,
Came the Lucky Shot right into Ranger;
Ranger swerving knocked Bitter Dick,
Who blundered at it and leaped too quick;
Then crash went Blackthorn as Bitter Dick fell,
Meringue jumped on him and rolled as well.
As Charles got over he splashed the dirt
Of the poor Turk's Grave on two men hurt.

Right Royal landed.

JOHN MASEFIELD

Puck's Song

SEE you the dimpled track that runs,
  All hollow through the wheat?
O that was where they hauled the guns
  That smote King Philip's fleet.

See you our little mill that clacks,
  So busy by the brook?
She has ground her corn and paid her tax
  Ever since Domesday Book.

See you our stilly woods of oak,
  And the dread ditch beside?
O that was where the Saxons broke
  On the day that Harold died.

See you the windy levels spread
      About the gates of Rye?
O that was where the Northmen fled,
      When Alfred's ships came by.

See you our pastures wide and lone,
      Where the red oxen browse?
O there was a City thronged and known,
      Ere London boasted a house.

And see you, after rain, the trace
      Of mound and ditch and wall?
O that was a Legion's camping-place,
      When Cæsar sailed from Gaul.

And see you marks that show and fade,
      Like shadows on the Downs?
O they are the lines the Flint Men made,
      To guard their wondrous towns.

Trackway and Camp and City lost,
      Salt Marsh where now is corn;
Old Wars, old Peace, old Arts that cease,
      And so was England born!

She is not any common Earth,
      Water or wood or air,
But Merlin's Isle of Gramarye,
      Where you and I will fare!

RUDYARD KIPLING

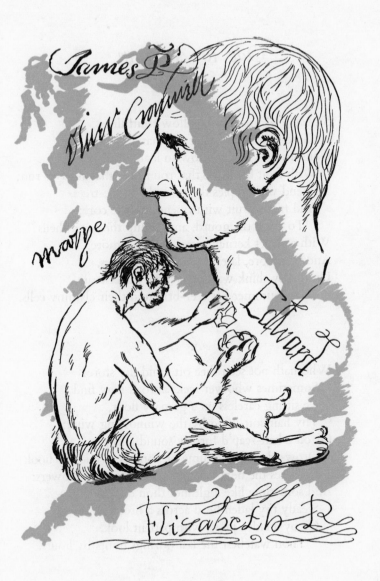

James R

Oliver Cromwell

marye

Edward

Elizabeth R

15

Ode to Autumn

I

SEASON of mists and mellow fruitfulness,
  Close bosom-friend of the maturing sun;
Conspiring with him how to load and bless
  With fruit the vines that round the thatch-eaves run;
To bend with apples the moss'd cottage-trees,
  And fill all fruit with ripeness to the core;
    To swell the gourd, and plump the hazel shells
With a sweet kernel; to set budding more,
And still more, later flowers for the bees,
Until they think warm days will never cease,
    For Summer has o'er-brimm'd their clammy cells.

II

Who hath not seen thee oft amid thy store?
  Sometimes whoever seeks abroad may find
Thee sitting careless on a granary floor,
  Thy hair soft-lifted by the winnowing wind;
Or on a half-reap'd furrow sound asleep,
  Drowsed with the fume of poppies, while thy hook
    Spares the next swath and all its twinèd flowers:
And sometime like a gleaner thou dost keep
  Steady thy laden head across a brook;
  Or by a cider-press, with patient look,
    Thou watchest the last oozings hours by hours.

Where are the songs of Spring? Ay, where are they?
  Think not of them, thou hast thy music too,—
While barrèd clouds bloom the soft-dying day,
  And touch the stubble-plains with rosy hue;
Then in a wailful choir the small gnats mourn
  Among the river sallows, borne aloft
    Or sinking as the light wind lives or dies;
And full-grown lambs loud bleat from hilly bourn;
  Hedge-crickets sing; and now with treble soft
  The redbreast whistles from a garden-croft;
    And gathering swallows twitter in the skies.

JOHN KEATS

Autumn

THE thistle down's flying, though the winds are all still,
On the green grass now lying, now mounting the hill,
The spring from the fountain now boils like a pot;
Through stones past the counting it bubbles red-hot.

The ground parched and cracked is like overbaked bread,
The greensward all wracked is, bents dried up and dead.
The fallow fields glitter like water indeed,
And gossamers twitter, flung from weed unto weed.

Hill tops like hot iron glitter bright in the sun,
And the rivers we're eying burn to gold as they run;
Burning hot is the ground, liquid gold is the air;
Whoever looks round sees Eternity there.

JOHN CLARE

The Knight's Tomb

WHERE is the grave of Sir Arthur O'Kellyn?
Where may the grave of that good man be—
By the side of a spring, on the breast of Helvellyn,
Under the twigs of a young birch tree!
    The oak that in summer was sweet to hear,
    And rustled its leaves in the fall of the year,
    And whistled and roared in the winter alone,
    Is gone—and the birch in its stead is grown.—
    The Knight's bones are dust,
    And his good sword rust;—
    His soul is with the saints, I trust.

SAMUEL TAYLOR COLERIDGE

18

A Dream

(from *King Richard III*)

LORD, Lord! methought, what pain it was to drown!
What dreadful noise of waters in mine ears!
What ugly sights of death within mine eyes!
Methought I saw a thousand fearful wracks;
Ten thousand men that fishes gnaw'd upon;
Wedges of gold, great anchors, heaps of pearl,
Inestimable stones, unvalued jewels,
All scattered in the bottom of the sea:
Some lay in dead men's skulls; and, in those holes
Where eyes did once inhabit, there were crept,
As 'twere in scorn of eyes, reflecting gems,
Which woo'd the slimy bottom of the deep,
And mock'd the dead bones that lay scattered by.

WILLIAM SHAKESPEARE

Badger

WHEN midnight comes a host of dogs and men
Go out and track the badger to his den,
And put a sack within the hole, and lie
Till the old grunting badger passes by.
He comes and hears—they let the strongest loose.
The old fox hears the noise and drops the goose.
The poacher shoots and hurries from the cry,
And the old hare half wounded buzzes by.
They get a forkèd stick to bear him down
And clap the dogs and take him to the town,
And bait him all the day with many dogs,
And laugh and shout and fright the scampering hogs.
He runs along and bites at all he meets:
They shout and hollo down the noisy streets.

He turns about to face the loud uproar
And drives the rebels to their very door.
The frequent stone is hurled where'er they go;
When badgers fight, then every one's a foe.
The dogs are clapt and urged to join the fray;
The badger turns and drives them all away.
Though scarcely half as big, demure and small,
He fights with dogs for hours and beats them all.
The heavy mastiff, savage in the fray,
Lies down and licks his feet and turns away.
The bulldog knows his match and waxes cold,
The badger grins and never leaves his hold.
He drives the crowd and follows at their heels
And bites them through—the drunkard swears and reels.

The frighted women take the boys away,
The blackguard laughs and hurries on the fray.
He tries to reach the woods, an awkward race,
But sticks and cudgels quickly stop the chase.
He turns agen and drives the noisy crowd
And beats the many dogs in noises loud.
He drives away and beats them every one,
And then they loose them all and set them on.
He falls as dead and kicked by boys and men,
Then starts and grins and drives the crowd agen;
Till kicked and torn and beaten out he lies
And leaves his hold and cackles, groans, and dies.

JOHN CLARE

The Moonlit Stream

A STREAM far off beneath the moon
    Flowed silver-bright and thin,
Winding its way like some slow tune
    Played on a violin.

The valley trees were hushed and still;
    The sky was pearly grey;
The moonlight slept upon the hill—
    As white as snow it lay.

Then softly from a ruined tower
    That rose beside the stream
A bell chimed out the midnight hour;
    And then—Oh, did I dream?—

Then all at once a long, black boat
    With neither sail nor oars
Down that bright stream began to float
    Between its shadowy shores.

No passenger nor steersman stirred
    On that enchanted thing;
But faint, unearthly-sweet, I heard
    A choir of voices sing.

It moved mysterious and serene,
    A sable-feathered swan;
It seemed the soul of some sad queen
    Was borne to Avalon.

So in my thoughts that shadowy boat
    Will sail the moonlit river,
And faintly I shall hear the note
    Of that sad choir for ever.

JAMES REEVES

An Old Soldier of the Queen's

OF an old soldier of the Queen's,
  With an old motley coat, and a Maumsie nose,
And an old jerkin that's out at the elbows,
And an old pair of boots, drawn on without hose,
Stuft with rags instead of toes;
    And an old soldier of the Queen's,
    And the Queen's old soldier.

With an old rusty sword that's hackt with blows,
And an old dagger to scare away the crows,
And an old horse that reels as he goes,
And an old saddle that no man knows,[1]
    And an old soldier of the Queen's,
    And the Queen's old soldier.

With his old gun, and his bandoliers,
And an old head-piece to keep warm his ears,
He's now rid to Bohemia to fight with his foes,
And he swears by his valour he'll have better clothes,
Or else he'll lose legs, arms, fingers, and toes,
And he'll come again, when no man knows,
    And an old soldier of the Queen's,
    And the Queen's old soldier.

[1] Would recognise   TRADITIONAL

Over the Hills and Far Away

HARK! now the drums beat up again,
For all true soldiers, gentlemen,
Then let us 'list, and march, I say,
Over the hills and far away.

> *O'er the hills and o'er the main*
> *To Flanders, Portugal and Spain,*
> *Queen Anne commands, and we'll obey,*
> *Over the hills and far away.*

All gentlemen that have a mind
To serve the Queen that's good and kind,
Come 'list and enter into pay
Then over the hills and far away.

> *O'er the hills . . .*

Here's forty shillings on the drum
For those that volunteers do come,
With shirts, and clothes and present pay,
When over the hills and far away.

> *O'er the hills . . .*

No more from sound of drum retreat,
While Marlborough and Galloway beat
The French and Spaniards every day
When over the hills and far away.

> *O'er the hills . . .*

He that is forced to go and fight
Will never get true honour by't,
While Volunteers shall win the day
When over the hills and far away.
     O'er the hills . . .

Come on then, boys, and you shall see
We every one shall captains be,
To dress and strut as well as they
When over the hills and far away.
     O'er the hills . . .

For if we go 'tis one to ten
But we'll return all gentlemen,
All gentlemen as well as they,
When over the hills and far away.
     O'er the hills . . .

What though our friends our absence mourn
We with all honour shall return,
And then we'll sing both night and day
Over the hills and far away.
     O'er the hills . . .

TRADITIONAL

High Germany

O POLLY, Love, O Polly, the rout has now begun,
And we must march away at the beating of the drum:
Go dress yourself in all your best and come along with me,
I'll take you to the cruel wars in High Germany.

O Harry, O Harry, you mind what I do say,
My feet they are so tender I cannot march away,
And besides, my dearest Harry, though I'm in love with thee,
How am I fit for cruel wars in High Germany?

I'll buy you a horse, my Love, and on it you shall ride,
And all my heart's delight shall be riding by your side;
We'll call at every ale-house, and drink when we are dry,
So quickly on the road, my Love, we'll marry by and by.

O cursed were cruel wars that ever they should rise,
And out of merry England press many a lad likewise.
They pressed young Harry from me, likewise my brothers
    three,
And sent them to the cruel wars in High Germany.

TRADITIONAL

28

Darby Kelly

MY grandsire beat a drum so neat,
His name was Darby Kelly, O!
No lad so true at rat-tat-too,
At roll call or reveille, O!
When Marlb'ro's fame first raised his name,
My grandad beat the point of war;
At Blenheim he, at Ramillie,
Made ears to tingle near and far;
For with his wrist, he'd such a twist,
The girls would cheer, you don't know how,
They laughed and cried, and sighed and died,
To hear him beat the row, dow, dow,
  With a row, dow, dow, with a row, dow, dow!
  To hear him beat the row, dow, dow!
  They laughed and cried, and sighed and died,
  To hear him beat the row, dow, dow!

A son he had, which was my dad,
As brisk a lad as any, O!
You e'er would know, tho' you should go
From Chester to Kilkenny, O!
When great Wolfe died, his country's pride,
To arms my dapper father beat;
Each dale and hill remembers still
How loud, how long, how strong, how neat.
With each drumstick he had the trick,
The girls would cheer, you don't know how,
Their eyes would glisten, their ears would listen,
To hear him beat the row, dow, dow,
  With a row, dow, dow, with a row, dow, dow!
  To hear him beat the row, dow, dow,
  They laughed and cried, and sighed and died,
  To hear him beat the row, dow, dow!

Ere I did wed, ne'er be it said,
But that the foe I dared to meet,
With Wellington, old Erin's son,
I helped to make them both retreat.
King Arthur once, or I'm a dunce,
Was called the hero of the age;
But what's he been to him we've seen,
The Arthur of the modern page?
For by the powers, from Lisbon's bowers,
He trophies bore to grace his brow,
He made Nap prance right out of France,
With his English, Irish, row, dow, dow,
  With a row, dow, dow, with a row, dow, dow!
  His English, Irish, row, dow, dow!
  His row, dow, dow, his row, dow, dow,
  His English, Irish, row, dow, dow!

TRADITIONAL

30

Seumas[1] Beg

A MAN was sitting underneath a tree
Outside the village; and he asked me what
Name was upon this place; and said that he
Was never here before—He told a lot

Of stories to me too. His nose was flat!
I asked him how it happened, and he said
—The first mate of the Holy Ghost did that
With a marling-spike one day; but he was dead,

And jolly good job too; and he'd have gone
A long way to have killed him—Oh, he had
A gold ring in one ear; the other one
—'Was bit off by a crocodile, bedad!'—

That's what he said. He taught me how to chew!
He was a real nice man! He liked me too!

JAMES STEPHENS

[1] *Seumas:* pronounced *Shamus.*

To the Four Courts, please

THE driver rubbed at his nettly chin
With a huge loose forefinger, crooked and black;
And his wobbly violet lips sucked in,
And puffed out again and hung down slack:
A black fang shone through his lop-sided smile,
In his little pouched eye flickered years of guile.

And the horse, poor beast! It was ribbed and forked;
And its ears hung down, and its eyes were old;
And its knees were knuckly; and as we talked,
It swung the stiff neck that could scarcely hold
Its big skinny head up—then I stepped in,
And the driver climbed to his seat with a grin.

God help the horse, and the driver too!
And the people and beasts who have never a friend!
For the driver easily might have been you,
And the horse be me by a different end!
And nobody knows how their days will cease!
And the poor, when they're old, have little of peace!

JAMES STEPHENS

Come, Come Away

COME, come away, to the tavern I say,
For now at home 'tis washing day;
Leave your prittle-prattle, and fill us a pottle,
You are not so wise as Aristotle.
Drawer come away, let's make it holy day:
Anon, anon, anon, Sir, what is't you say?

TRADITIONAL

The Briery Bush

O the briery bush,
That pricks my heart so sore;
If I once get out of the briery bush,
I'll never get in any more.

'O hangman stay thy hand,
  And stay it for a while,
For I fancy I see my father a-coming
  Across the yonder stile.
Father have you brought my gold?
  And can you set me free?
Or are you come to see me hung
  All on the gallows tree?'
'I've not brought thee gold,
  And I can't set thee free;
But I have come to see thee hung
  All on the gallows tree.'

O the briery . . .

'O hangman stay thy hand,
  And stay it for a while,
For I fancy I see my mother a-coming
  Across the yonder stile.
Mother have you brought my gold?
  And can you set me free?
Or are you come to see me hung
  All on the gallows tree?'

33

'I've not brought thee gold,
    And I can't set thee free;
But I have come to see thee hung
    All on the gallows tree.'

O the briery . . .

'O hangman stay thy hand,
    And stay it for a while,
For I fancy I see my true-love a-coming
    Across the yonder stile.
O true-love have you my gold?
    And can you set me free?
Or are you come to see me hung
    All on the gallows tree?'
'O yes, I've brought thee gold,
    And I can set thee free;
And I've not come to see thee hung
    All on the gallows tree.'

O the briery bush,
That pricks my heart so sore;
Now I've got out of the briery bush,
I'll never get in any more.

TRADITIONAL

Boney was a Warrior

BONEY was a warrior,
    Way-ay yah,
Boney was a warrior,
    John Fran-swah.

34

Boney beat the Prooshians,
Boney beat the Rooshians.

Boney went to Moscow,
Moscow was afire.

Boney he came back again,
Boney he came back again.

Boney went to Elbow,
Boney went to Elbow.

Boney went to Waterloo,
Boney was defeated.

Boney was a prisoner,
'Board the Billy Ruffian.

Boney he was sent away,
'Way to St. Helena.

Boney broke his heart and died,
Boney broke his heart and died.

Boney was a warrior,
Way-ay yah,
Boney was a warrior,
John Fran-swah.

TRADITIONAL

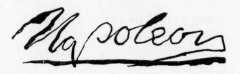

THE BATTLE OF THE NILE, 1798
engraving by Daniel Orme, published 1805

The Old Navy

THE captain stood on the carronade: 'First lieutenant,' says he,
'Send all my merry men aft here, for they must list to me;
I haven't the gift of the gab, my sons—because I'm bred to the
    sea;
That ship there is a Frenchman, who means to fight with we.
    And odds bobs, hammer and tongs, long as I've been to sea,
    I've fought 'gainst every odds—but I've gain'd the victory!

'That ship there is a Frenchman, and if we don't take she,
'Tis a thousand bullets to one, that she will capture we;
I haven't the gift of the gab, my boys; so each man to his gun;
If she's not mine in half an hour, I'll flog each mother's son.
    For odds bobs, hammer and tongs, long as I've been to sea,
    I've fought 'gainst every odds—and I've gain'd the victory!'

We fought for twenty minutes, when the Frenchman had enough;
'I little thought,' said he, 'that your men were of such stuff';
Our captain took the Frenchman's sword, a low bow made to
    he;
'I haven't the gift of the gab, monsieur, but polite I wish to be.
    And odds bobs, hammer and tongs, long as I've been to sea,
    I've fought 'gainst every odds—and I've gain'd the victory!'

Our captain sent for all of us: 'My merry men,' said he,
'I haven't the gift of the gab, my lads, but yet I thankful be:
You've done your duty handsomely, each man stood to his gun;
If you hadn't, you villains, as sure as day, I'd have flogg'd each
    mother's son,
    For odds bobs, hammer and tongs, as long as I'm at sea,
    I'll fight 'gainst every odds—and I'll gain the victory!'

FREDERICK MARRYAT

Mariners' Song

To sea, to sea! The calm is o'er;
  The wanton water leaps in sport,
And rattles down the pebbly shore;
  The dolphin wheels, the sea-cows snort,
And unseen Mermaids' pearly song
Comes bubbling up, the weeds among.
  Fling broad the sail, dip deep the oar:
  To sea, to sea! the calm is o'er.

To sea, to sea! our wide-wing'd bark
  Shall billowy cleave its sunny way,
And with its shadow, fleet and dark,
  Break the caved Titons' azure day,
Like mighty eagle soaring light
O'er antelopes on Alpine height.
  The anchor heaves, the ship swings free,
  The sails swell full. To sea, to sea!

THOMAS LOVELL BEDDOES

Casey Jones

COME all you rounders listen here
I'll tell you the story of a brave engineer;
Casey Jones was the hogger's name,
On a six-eight-wheeler, boys, he won his fame.
Caller called Casey at half-past four,
He kissed his wife at the station door,
Mounted to the cabin with orders in his hand,
And took his farewell trip to the promised land.

> *Casey Jones, mounted to the cabin,*
> *Casey Jones, with his orders in his hand!*
> *Casey Jones, mounted to the cabin,*
> *Took his farewell trip into the promised land.*

'Put in your water and shovel in your coal,
Put your head out the window, watch the drivers roll,
I'll run her till she leaves the rail,
'Cause we're eight hours late with the Western Mail!'
He looked at his watch and his watch was slow,
Looked at the water and the water was low,
Turned to his fireboy and then he said,
'We're bound to reach 'Frisco, but we'll all be dead!'

> *Casey Jones, mounted . . .*

Casey pulled up Reno Hill,
Tooted for the crossing with an awful shrill.
Snakes all knew by the engine's moans
That the hogger at the throttle was Casey Jones.
He pulled up short two miles from the place,
Freight train stared him right in the face,
Turned to his fireboy, 'Sim, you'd better jump,
'Cause there's two locomotives that's going to bump!'

> *Casey Jones, mounted . . .*

Casey said, just before he died,
'There's two more roads I'd like to ride.'
Fireboy he asked, 'What can they be?'
'The Rio Grande and the Santa Fe.'
Mrs Jones sat on her bed a-sighing,
Got a pink that Casey was dying,
Said, 'Hush you, children, stop your crying,
'Cause you'll get another papa on the Salt Lake line.'

> *Casey Jones, mounted . . .*

TRADITIONAL

The Streets of Laredo

As I walked out in the streets of Laredo,
    As I walked out in Laredo one day,
I spied a poor cowboy wrapped up in white linen,
    Wrapped up in white linen and cold as the clay.

'I see by your outfit that you are a cowboy,'
    These words he did say as I boldly stepped by.
'Come, sit down beside me and hear my sad story;
    I was shot in the breast and I know I must die.

'Once in my saddle I used to look handsome,
    Once in my saddle I used to look gay.
I first went to drinking and then to card-playing,
    Got shot in the breast, which ended my day.

'Let sixteen gamblers come handle my coffin,
    Let sixteen girls come carry my pall;
Put bunches of roses all over my coffin,
    Put roses to deaden the clods as they fall.

'And beat the drum slowly and play the fife lowly,
    And play the dead march as you carry me along;
Take me to the prairie and lay the turf o'er me,
    For I'm a young cowboy and I know I've done wrong.'

We beat the drum slowly and played the fife lowly,
    And bitterly wept as we bore him along;
For we all loved our comrade, so brave, young and
      handsome,
    We loved the young cowboy, although he'd done wrong.

TRADITIONAL

John Henry

(John Henry, a negro worker—real or legendary—in the early
days of the American railways, is the hero of countless songs and
ballads.)

> JOHN HENRY was a little baby,
> Sitting on his mammy's knee,
> He gave one long and lonesome cry,
> Said: 'That hammer'll be the death of me.'

> Captain said to John Henry:
> 'Gonna bring me a steam drill round.
> Gonna take that steam drill out on the job,
> Gonna whop that steel on down.'

> John Henry told his captain,
> Lightning was in his eye:
> 'I'll never be conquered by your old steam drill.
> I'll beat it to the bottom or I'll die.'

> John Henry walked in the tunnel,
> Had his captain by his side;
> But the rock so tall, John Henry so small,
> Lord, he laid down his hammer and he cried.

> Now John Henry start on the right hand,
> The steam drill start on the left.
> 'Before I let this steam drill beat me down,
> I'd hammer myself to death.'

Well, John Henry kissed his hammer;
   The white man turned on the steam;
Little Bill held John Henry's trusty steel;
   Was the biggest race the world ever seen.

Now John Henry swung his hammer
   And he brought it down on the ground,
And a man in Chatanooga two hundred mile away
   Thought he heard a sobbing sound.

Oh, the captain said to John Henry:
   'I believe this mountain's falling in.'
John Henry said to his captain:
   ''Tain't nothin' but my hammer suckin' wind.'

John Henry said as he took his stand:
   'This'll be the end of me.'
But every foot that steam drill drove
   John Henry's hammer drove three.

John Henry was hammering on the mountain,
   And his hammer was striking fire.
He drove so hard till he broke his heart,
   And he lay down his hammer and he died.

When John Henry died there wasn't no box
   Was big enough to hold his bones.
So they buried him in a boxcar[1] deep in the ground,
   Let two mountains be his grave stones.

[1] Goods wagon.

TRADITIONAL

Verses from 'Greensleeves'

GREENSLEEVES was all my joy,
Greensleeves was my delight;
Greensleeves was my heart of gold,
And who but Lady Greensleeves.

Alas, my Love! ye do me wrong
To cast me off discourteously;
And I have lovèd you so long,
Delighting in your company.

I have been ready at your hand,
To grant whatever you would crave;
I have both waged life and land,
Your love and goodwill for to have.

I bought thee petticoats of the best,
The cloth so fine as fine might be;
I gave thee jewels for thy chest,
And all this cost I spent on thee.

Thy gown was of the grassy green,
Thy sleeves of satin hanging by,
Which made thee be our harvest queen,
And yet thou wouldst not love me.

My gayest gelding I thee gave,
To ride wherever likèd thee;
No lady ever was so brave,
And yet thou wouldst not love me.

My men were clothèd all in green,
And they did ever wait on thee;
And this was gallant to be seen,
And yet thou wouldst not love me.

They set thee up, they took thee down,
They served thee with humility;
Thy foot might not once touch the ground,
And yet thou wouldst not love me.

For every morning when thou rose,
I sent thee dainties orderly,
To cheer thy stomach from all woes,
And yet thou wouldst not love me.

Well, I will pray to God on high,
That thou my constancy mayst see,
And that yet once before I die,
Thou wilt vouchsafe to love me.

TRADITIONAL

Green Grow the Rushes Ho!

I'LL sing you One, ho!
  Green grow the rushes ho!
 What is your One, ho?
One is One and all alone and ever more shall *be* so.

I'll sing you Two, ho!
  Green grow the rushes ho!
 What are your Two, ho?
Two, two the lily-white boys, clothèd all in green, ho!
One is One and all alone and ever more shall *be* so.

I'll sing you Three, ho!
Green grow the rushes ho!
What are your Three, ho?
Three, three the rivals,
Two, two the lily-white boys, clothèd all in green, ho!
One is One and all alone and ever more shall *be* so.

I'll sing you Four, ho!
Green grow the rushes ho!
What are your Four, ho?
Four for the gospel-makers,
Three, three the rivals,
Two, two the lily-white boys, clothèd all in green, ho!
One is One and all alone and ever more shall *be* so.

I'll sing you Five, ho!
Green grow the rushes ho!
What are your Five, ho?
Five for the symbols at your door,
And Four for the gospel-makers,
Three, three the rivals,
Two, two the lily-white boys, clothèd all in green, ho!
One is One and all alone and ever more shall *be* so.

I'll sing you Six, ho!
Green grow the rushes ho!
What are your Six, ho?
Six for the six proud walkers,
Five for the symbols at your door,
And Four for the gospel-makers,
Three, three the rivals,
Two, two the lily-white boys, clothèd all in green, ho!
One is One and all alone and ever more shall *be* so.

I'll sing you Seven, ho!
Green grow the rushes ho!
What are your Seven, ho?
Seven for the seven stars in the sky,
And Six for the six proud walkers,
Five for the symbols at your door,
And Four for the gospel-makers,
Three, three the rivals,
Two, two the lily-white boys, clothèd all in green, ho!
One is One and all alone and ever more shall *be* so.

I'll sing you Eight, ho!
Green grow the rushes ho!
What are your Eight, ho?
Eight for the April rainers,
Seven for the seven stars in the sky,
And Six for the six proud walkers,
Five for the symbols at your door,
Four for the gospel-makers,
Three, three the rivals,
Two, two the lily-white boys, clothèd all in green, ho!
One is One and all alone and ever more shall *be* so.

I'll sing you Nine, ho!
Green grow the rushes ho!
What are your Nine, ho?
Nine for the nine bright shiners,
Eight for the April rainers,
Seven for the seven stars in the sky,
And Six for the six proud walkers,
Five for the symbols at your door,
Four for the gospel-makers,
Three, three the rivals,
Two, two the lily-white boys, clothèd all in green, ho!
One is One and all alone and ever more shall *be* so.

I'll sing you Ten, ho!
Green grow the rushes ho!
What are your Ten, ho?
Ten for the ten commandments,
Nine for the nine bright shiners,
Eight for the April rainers,
Seven for the seven stars in the sky,
And Six for the six proud walkers,
Five for the symbols at your door,
Four for the gospel-makers,
Three, three the rivals,
Two, two the lily-white boys, clothèd all in green, ho!
One is One and all alone and ever more shall *be* so.

I'll sing you Eleven, ho!
  Green grow the rushes ho!
 What are your Eleven, ho?
Eleven for the eleven went up to Heaven,
And Ten for the ten commandments,
Nine for the nine bright shiners,
Eight for the April rainers,
Seven for the seven stars in the sky,
And Six for the six proud walkers,
Five for the symbols at your door,
And Four for the gospel-makers,
Three, three the rivals,
Two, two the lily-white boys, clothèd all in green, ho!
One is One and all alone and ever more shall *be* so.

I'll sing you Twelve, ho!
  Green grow the rushes ho!
 What are your Twelve, ho!
Twelve for the twelve Apostles,
Eleven for the eleven went up to Heaven,
And Ten for the ten commandments,
Nine for the nine bright shiners,
Eight for the April rainers,
Seven for the seven stars in the sky,
And Six for the six proud walkers,
Five for the symbols at your door,
And Four for the gospel-makers,
Three, three the rivals,
Two, two the lily-white boys, clothèd all in green, ho!
One is One and all alone and ever more shall *be* so.

TRADITIONAL

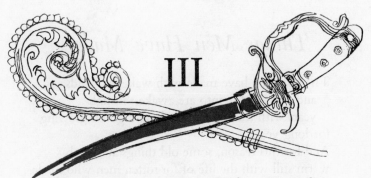

III

Fighting South of the Castle

THEY fought south of the Castle,
They died north of the wall.
They died in the moors and were not buried.
Their flesh was the food of crows.
'Tell the crows we are not afraid;
We have died in the moors and cannot be buried.
Crows, how can our bodies escape you?'
The waters flowed deep
And the rushes in the pool were dark.
The riders fought and were slain:
Their horses wander neighing.
By the bridge there was a house.
Was it south, was it north?
The harvest was never gathered.
How can we give you your offerings?
You served your Prince faithfully,
Though all in vain.
I think of you, faithful soldiers;
Your service shall not be forgotten.
For in the morning you went out to battle
And at night you did not return.

ARTHUR WALEY

Things Men Have Made

THINGS men have made with wakened hands,
    and put soft life into are awake through
    years with transferred touch, and go on glowing
for long years.
And for this reason, some old things are lovely
warm still with the life of forgotten men who made
    them.

DAVID HERBERT LAWRENCE

The Old Workman

'WHY are you so bent down before your time,
Old Mason? Many have not left their prime
So far behind at your age, and can still
    Stand full upright at will.'

He pointed to the mansion front hard by,
And to the stones of the quoin against the sky;
'Those upper blocks,' he said, 'that there you see,
    It was *that* ruined me.'

There stood in the air up to the parapet
Crowning the corner height, the stones as set
By him—ashlar whereon the gales might drum
    For centuries to come.

'I carried them up,' he said, 'by a ladder there;
The last was as big a load as I could bear;
But on I heaved; and something in my back
    Moved, as 'twere with a crack.'

D. H. LAWRENCE: 1922

portrait sketch by Jan Juta

'So I got crockt. I never lost that sprain;
And those who live there, walled from wind and rain
By freestone that I lifted, do not know
        That my life's ache came so.

'They don't know me, or even know my name,
But good I think it, somehow, all the same
To have kept 'em safe from harm, and right and tight,
        Though it has broke me quite.

'Yes; that I fixed it firm up there I am proud,
Facing the hail and snow and sun and cloud,
And to stand storms for ages, beating round
        When I lie underground.'

THOMAS HARDY

A Child's Pet

WHEN I sailed out of Baltimore,
With twice a thousand head of sheep,
They would not eat, they would not drink,
But bleated o'er the deep.

Inside the pens we crawled each day,
To sort the living from the dead;
And when we reached the Mersey's mouth,
Had lost five hundred head.

Yet every night and day one sheep,
That had no fear of man or sea,
Stuck through the bars its pleading face,
And it was stroked by me.

And to the sheep-men standing near,
'You see,' I said, 'this one tame sheep?
It seems a child has lost her pet,
And cried herself to sleep.'

So every time we passed it by,
Sailing to England's slaughter-house,
Eight ragged sheep-men—tramps and thieves—
Would stroke that sheep's black nose.

WILLIAM HENRY DAVIES

Peace

My soul, there is a country
  Far beyond the stars,
Where stands a wingèd sentry
  All skilful in the wars:
There, above noise and danger,
  Sweet Peace sits, crown'd with smiles,
And One born in a manger
  Commands the beauteous files.
He is thy gracious Friend,
  And—O my soul, awake!—
Did in pure love descend
  To die here for thy sake.
If thou can get but thither,
  There grows the flower of Peace,
The Rose that cannot wither,
  Thy fortress, and thy ease.
Leave then thy foolish ranges;
  For none can thee secure
But One who never changes—
  Thy God, thy life, thy cure.

HENRY VAUGHAN

55

Praise

KING of glory, King of peace,
    I will love Thee;
And, that love may never cease,
    I will move Thee.

Thou hast granted my request,
    Thou hast heard me;
Thou didst note my working breast,
    Thou hast spared me.

Wherefore with my utmost art
    I will sing Thee,
And the cream of all my heart
    I will bring Thee.

Though my sins against me cried,
    Thou didst clear me;
And alone, when they replied,
    Thou didst hear me.

Seven whole days, not one in seven,
    I will praise Thee;
In my heart, though not in heaven,
    I can raise Thee.

Thou grew'st soft and moist with tears
    Thou relentedst,
And when justice called for fears
    Thou dissentedst.

Small it is in this poor sort
    To enrol Thee;
Even eternity is too short
    To extol Thee.

GEORGE HERBERT

Jerusalem, My Happy Home

JERUSALEM, my happy home,
  When shall I come to thee?
When shall my sorrows have an end?
  Thy joys when shall I see?

In thee no sickness may be seen,
  No hurt, no ache, no sore;
There is no death nor ugly dev'l,
  There's life for evermore.

No dampish mist is seen in thee,
  No cold nor darksome night;
There every soul shines as the sun;
  There God himself gives light.

There lust and lucre cannot dwell;
  There envy bears no sway;
There is no hunger, heat, nor cold,
  But pleasure every way.

Thy walls are made of precious stones,
  Thy bulwarks diamonds square;
Thy gates are of right orient pearl;
  Exceeding rich and rare;

Thy turrets and thy pinnacles
  With carbuncles do shine;
Thy very streets are paved with gold,
  Surpassing clear and fine;

Within thy gates no thing doth come
    That is not passing clean,
No spider's web, no dirt, no dust,
    No filth may there be seen.

Thy gardens and thy gallant walks
    Continually are green;
There grows such sweet and pleasant flowers
    As nowhere else are seen.

Thy houses are of ivory,
    Thy windows crystal clear;
Thy tiles are made of beaten gold—
    O God that I were there!

Quite through the streets, with silver sound,
    The flood of life doth flow;
Upon whose banks on every side
    The wood of life doth grow.

There trees for evermore bear fruit,
    And evermore do spring;
There evermore the angels sit,
    And evermore do sing.

Ah, my sweet home, Jerusalem,
    Would God I were in thee!
Would God my woes were at an end,
    Thy joys that I might see!

ANONYMOUS

IV

The Crocodile

Now listen you landsmen unto me, to tell you the truth I'm
    bound,
What happened to me by going to sea, and the wonders that I
    found;
Shipwrecked I was once off Perouse and cast upon the shore,
So then I did resolve to roam, the country to explore.

'Twas far I had not scouted out, when close alongside the ocean,
I saw something move which at first I thought was all the world
    in motion;
But steering up close alongside, I found 'twas a crocodile,
And from his nose to the tip of his tail he measured five hundred
    mile.

While up aloft the wind was high, it blew a gale from the south,
I lost my hold and away did fly right into the crocodile's mouth,
He quickly closed his jaws on me and thought he'd got a victim,
But I ran down his throat, d'ye see, and that's the way I tricked
    him.

I travelled on for a month or two, till I got into his maw,
Where I found of rum-kegs not a few, and a thousand fat
    bullocks in store.
Of life I banished all my care, for of grub I was not stinted,
And in this crocodile I lived ten years, and very well contented.

This crocodile being very old, one day, alas, he died;
He was ten long years a-getting cold, he was so long and wide.
His skin was eight miles thick, I'm sure, or very near about,
For I was full ten years or more a-cutting my way out.

And now I've once more got on earth, I've vow'd no more to
    roam,
In a ship that passed I got a berth, and now I'm safe at home.
And if my story you should doubt, should ever travel the Nile,
It's ten to one you'll find the shell of the wonderful crocodile.

ANONYMOUS

The Wife of Usher's Well

THERE lived a wife at Usher's Well,
  And a wealthy wife was she;
She had three stout and stalwart sons,
  And sent them o'er the sea.

They hadna been a week from her,
  A week but barely ane,
When word came to the carlin[1] wife,
  That her three sons were gane.

They hadna been a week from her,
  A week but barely three,
When word came to the carlin wife,
  That her sons she'd never see.

'I wish the wind may never cease,
  Nor fashes[2] in the flood,
Till my three sons come hame to me,
  In earthly flesh and blood!'

It fell about the Martinmas,
  When nights are lang and mirk,
The carlin wife's three sons came hame,
  And their hats were o' the birk.[3]

It neither grew in dyke nor ditch,
  Nor yet in ony sheugh;[4]
But at the gates o' Paradise,
  That birk grew fair eneugh.

[1] Old. [2] Troubles. [3] Birch. [4] Trench.

'Blow up the fire, my maidens,
   Bring water from the well!
For a' my house shall feast this night,
   Since my three sons are well.'

And she has made to them a bed,
   She's made it large and wide;
And she's ta'en her mantle her about,
   Sat down at the bedside.

Up then crew the red red cock,
   And up and crew the gray;
The eldest to the youngest said,
   "Tis time we were away.'

The cock he hadna craw'd but once,
   And clapp'd his wings at a',
When the youngest to the eldest said,
   'Brother, we must awa.

'The cock doth craw, the day doth daw,
   The channerin' worm[1] doth chide;
Gin we be mist out o' our place,
   A sair pain we maun bide.

'Fare ye weel, my mother dear!
   Fareweel to barn and byre!
And fare ye weel, the bonny lass,
   That kindles my mother's fire.'

[1] Fretting serpent.

TRADITIONAL

Stanzas from 'The Faerie Queene'

The Dragon

By this the dreadful beast drew nigh to hand,
Half flying, and half footing in his haste,
That with his largeness measurèd much land,
And made wide shadow under his huge waist;
As mountain doth the valley overcast.
Approaching nigh, he rearèd high afore
His body monstrous, horrible, and vast,
Which, to increase his wondrous greatness more,
Was swoll'n with wrath, and poison, and with bloody gore.

And over, all with brazen scales was armed,
Like plated coat of steel, so couchèd near,
That nought might pierce, ne might his corse be harmed
With dint of sword, nor push of pointed spear;
Which as an eagle, seeing prey appear,
His airy plumes doth rouse, full rudely dight,[1]
So shakèd he, that horror was to hear,
For as the clashing of an armour bright,
Such noise his rousèd scales did send unto the knight.

His flaggy wings which forth he did display,
Were like two sails, in which the hollow wind
Is gathered full, and worketh speedy way;
And eke the pennes,[2] that did his pinions bind,
Were like mainyards, with flying canvas lined,
With which whenas him list the air to beat,
And there by force unwonted passage find
The clouds before him fled for terror great,
And all the heavens stood still amazèd with his threat.

[1] Roughly displayed.　　　　　[2] Feathers.

65

His huge long tail wound up in hundred folds
Does overspread his long brass-scaly back
Whose wreathèd bouts[1] whenever he unfolds
And thick entangled knots adown does slack,
Bespotted as with shields of red and black,
It sweepeth all the land behind him far
And off three furlongs does but little lack;
And at the point two stings infixèd are,
Both deadly sharp, that sharpest steel exceeden far.

But stings and sharpest steel did far exceed
The sharpness of his cruel rending claws;
Dead was it sure, as sure as death indeed,
Whatever thing does touch his ravenous paws,
Or what within his reach he ever draws.
But his most hideous head my tongue to tell
Does tremble: for his deep devouring jaws
Wide gapèd, like the grisly mouth of hell,
Through which into his dark abyss all ravin[2] fell.

And that more wondrous was, in either jaw
Three ranks of iron teeth enrangèd were,
In which yet trickling blood and gobbets raw
Of late devourèd bodies did appear,
That sight thereof bred cold congealèd fear:
Which to increase, and all at once to kill,
A cloud of smothering smoke and sulphur sere[3]
Out of his stinking gorge forth steamèd still
That all the air about with smoke and stench did fill.

[1] Coils.   [2] Prey.   [3] Burning.

His blazing eyes, like two bright shining shields,
Did burn with wrath, and sparkled living fire;
As two broad beacons set in open fields,
Send forth their flames far off to every shire,
And warning give, that enemies conspire,
With fire and sword the region to invade;
So flamed his eyes with rage and rancorous ire:
But far within, as in a hollow glade,
Those glaring lamps were set, that made a dreadful shade.

THE DRAGON WOUNDED

So dreadfully he towards him did pass,
Fore-lifting up aloft his speckled breast,
And often bounding on the bruisèd grass,
As for great joyance of his new-come guest.
Eftsoons[1] he gan advance his haughty crest,
As chafèd boar his bristles doth uprear,
And shook his scales to battle ready dressed
That made the red cross knight nigh quake for fear,
As bidding bold defiance to his foeman near.

The knight 'gan fairly couch his steady spear,
And fiercely ran at him with rigorous might:
The pointed steel arriving rudely there,
His harder hide would neither pierce, nor bite,
But glancing by forth passèd forward right;
Yet sore a-movèd with so puissant[2] push,
The wrathful beast about him turnèd light,
And him so rudely passing by, did brush
With his long tail, that horse and man to ground did rush.

[1] Forthwith.   [2] Mighty.

Both horse and man up lightly rose again,
And fresh encounter towards him addressed.
But th'idle stroke yet back recoiled in vain,
And found no place his deadly point to rest.
Exceeding rage enflamed the furious beast,
To be avengèd of so great despite;
For never felt his imperceable[1] breast
So wondrous force, from hand of living wight;
Yet had he proved the power of many a puissant[2] knight.

Then with his waving wings displayèd wide,
Himself up high he lifted from the ground,
And with strong flight did forcibly divide
The yielding air, which nigh too feeble found
Her flitting parts, and element unsound,
To bear so great a weight: he cutting way
With his broad sails, about him soarèd round:
At last low stooping with unwieldy sway,
Snatched up both horse and man, to bear them quite away.

Long he them bore above the subject plain,
So far as yewen bow a shaft may send,
Till struggling strong him did at last constrain,
To let them down before his flightès end:
As haggard hawk presuming to contend
With hardy fowl above his able might,
His weary pounces[3] all in vain doth spend,
To truss the prey too heavy for his flight;
Which coming down to ground does free itself by fight.

[1] Impenetrable.   [2] Mighty.   [3] Claws.

68

He so disseizèd of his gryping gross,[1]
The knight his thrillant[2] spear again assayed
In his brass plated body to emboss,[3]
And three men's strength unto the stroke he laid;
Wherewith the stiff beam quakèd, as afraid,
And glancing from his scaly neck did glide
Close under his left wing, then broad displayed.
The piercing steel there wrought a wound full wide,
That with the uncouth[4] smart the monster loudly cried.

He cried, as raging seas are wont to roar,
When wintry storm his wrathful wreck doth threat,
The rolling billows beat the ragged shore,
As they the earth would shoulder from her seat,
And greedy gulf does gape, as he would eat
His neighbour element in his revenge:
Then 'gin the blust'ring brethren boldly threat,
To move the world from off his steadfast hinge,
And boist'rous battle make, each other to avenge.

The steely head stuck fast still in his flesh,
Till with his cruel claws he snatched the wood,
And quite asunder broke. Forth flowèd fresh
A gushing river of black gory blood,
That drownèd all the land, whereon he stood;
The stream thereof would drive a water mill.
Trebly augmented was his furious mood
With bitter sense of his deep rooted ill,
That flames of fire he threw forth from his large nostril.

EDMUND SPENSER

[1] The dragon's mighty grip being broken.   [2] Piercing.   [3] Plunge.
[4] Unaccustomed.

The Forsaken Merman

COME, dear children, let us away;
    Down and away below.
Now my brothers call from the bay;
    Now the great winds shorewards blow;
    Now the salt tides seawards flow;
Now the wild white horses play,
Champ and chafe and toss in the spray.
Children dear, let us away.
    This way, this way.

Call her once before you go.
    Call once yet.
In a voice that she will know:
    'Margaret! Margaret!'
Children's voices should be dear
(Call once more) to a mother's ear:
Children's voices, wild with pain.
Surely she will come again.
Call her once and come away.
    This way, this way.
'Mother dear, we cannot stay.'
The wild white horses foam and fret.
    Margaret! Margaret!

Come, dear children, come away down.
    Call no more.
One last look at the white-walled town,
And the little grey church on the windy shore.
    Then come down.
She will not come though you call all day.
    Come away, come away.

Children dear, was it yesterday
We heard the sweet bells over the bay?
In the caverns where we lay,
Through the surf and through the swell,
The far-off sound of a silver bell?
Sand-strewn caverns, cool and deep,
Where the winds are all asleep;
Where the spent lights quiver and gleam;
Where the salt weed sways in the stream;
Where the sea-beasts ranged all round
Feed in the ooze of their pasture-ground;
Where the sea-snakes coil and twine,
Dry their mail and bask in the brine;
Where great whales come sailing by,
Sail and sail, with unshut eye,
Round the world for ever and aye?
When did music come this way?
Children dear, was it yesterday?

Children dear, was it yesterday
(Call yet once) that she went away?
Once she sate with you and me,
On a red gold throne in the heart of the sea,
And the youngest sate on her knee.
She combed its bright hair, and she tended it well,
When down swung the sound of the far-off bell.

She sigh'd, she looked up through the clear green sea.
She said, 'I must go, for my kinsfolk pray
In the little grey church on the shore to-day.
'Twill be Easter-time in the world—ah me!
And I lose my poor soul, Merman, here with thee.'
I said, 'Go up, dear heart, through the waves;
Say thy prayer, and come back to the kind sea-caves.'
She smiled, she went up through the surf in the bay.
Children dear, was it yesterday?

Children dear, were we long alone?
'The sea grows stormy, the little ones moan.
Long prayers,' I said, 'in the world they say.
Come!' I said, and we rose through the surf in the bay.
We went up the beach, by the sandy down
Where the sea-stocks bloom, to the white-walled town.
Through the narrow paved streets, where all was still,
To the little grey church on the windy hill.
From the church came a murmur of folk at their prayers,
But we stood without in the cold-blowing airs.
We climbed on the graves, on the stones worn with
    rains,
And we gazed up the aisle through the small-leaded
    panes.
She sate by the pillar; we saw her clear:
'Margaret, hist! come quick, we are here.
Dear heart,' I said, 'we are long alone.
The sea grows stormy, the little ones moan.'
But ah, she gave me never a look.
For her eyes were sealed to the holy book.
Loud prays the priest; shut stands the door.
Come away, children, call no more!
Come away, come down, call no more!

Down, down, down.
Down to the depths of the sea.
She sits at her wheel in the humming town,
Singing most joyfully.
Hark what she sings: 'O joy, O joy,
For the humming street, and the child with its toy.
For the priest, and the bell, and the holy well.
For the wheel where I spun,
And the blessed light of the sun.'
And so she sings her fill,
Singing most joyfully,
Till the shuttle falls from her hand,
And the whizzing wheel stands still.

She steals to the window, and looks at the sand,
And over the sand at the sea;
And her eyes are set in a stare;
And anon there breaks a sigh,
And anon there drops a tear,
From a sorrow-clouded eye,
And a heart sorrow-laden,
A long, long sigh;
For the cold, strange eyes of a little Mermaiden,
And the gleam of her golden hair.

Come away, away, children!
Come, children, come down!
The hoarse wind blows colder;
Lights shine in the town.
She will start from her slumber
When gusts shake the door;
She will hear the winds howling,
Will hear the waves roar.

We shall see, while above us
　　The waves roar and whirl,
A ceiling of amber,
　　A pavement of pearl.
Singing: 'Here came a mortal,
　　But faithless was she.
And alone dwell for ever
　　The kings of the sea.'

But, children, at midnight,
　　When soft the winds blow,
When clear falls the moonlight,
　　When spring-tides are low;
When sweet airs come seaward
　　From heaths starred with broom,
And high rocks throw mildly
　　On the blanched sands a gloom;
Up the still, glistening beaches,
　　Up the creeks we will hie,
Over banks of bright seaweed
　　The ebb-tide leaves dry.
We will gaze, from the sand-hills,
At the white, sleeping town,
At the church on the hillside—
　　And then come back down.
Singing: 'There dwells a loved one,
　　But cruel is she!
She left lonely for ever
　　The kings of the sea.'

MATTHEW ARNOLD

74

As Joseph was a-Walking

As Joseph was a-walking,
    He heard an angel sing—
'This night shall be born
    Our heavenly King;

'He neither shall be born
    In housen nor in hall,
Nor in the place of Paradise,
    But in an ox's stall;

'He neither shall be clothed
    In purple nor in pall,
But all in fair linen,
    As were babies all:

'He neither shall be rocked
    In silver nor in gold,
But in a wooden cradle,
    That rocks on the mould;

'He neither shall be christened
   In white wine nor in red,
But with the spring water
   With which we were christened.'

Then Mary took her young Son,
   And set Him on her knee—
'I pray thee now, dear Child,
   Tell how this world shall be?'

'This world shall be like
   The stones in the street,
For the sun and the moon
   Shall bow down at thy feet;

'And upon a Wednesday
   My vow I will make,
And upon Good Friday
   My death I will take;

'And upon the third day
   My uprising shall be,
And the sun and the moon
   Shall rise up with Me.'

TRADITIONAL

The Duke of Gordon's Daughter

THE Duke of Gordon had three daughters,
    Elizabeth, Marg'ret and Jean;
They would not stay in bonnie Castle Gordon,
    But they went to bonny Aberdeen.

They had not been in bonny Aberdeen
    A twelvemonth and a day,
Lady Jean fell in love with Captain Ogilvie
    And awa' with him she would gae.

Word came to the Duke of Gordon,
    In the chamber where he lay,
Lady Jean was in love with Captain Ogilvie,
    And from him she would not stay.

'Go saddle to me the black horse,
    And you'll ride on the grey,
And I will gang to bonny Aberdeen
    Forthwith to bring her away.'

They were not a mile from Aberdeen,
    A mile but only one,
Till he met with his two daughters,
    But awa' was Lady Jean.

'Where is your sister, maidens?
    Where is your sister now?
Say, what is become of your sister,
    That she is not walking with you?'

'O pardon us, honour'd father,
    O pardon us!' they did say;
'Lady Jean is wed with Captain Ogilvie,
    And from him she will not stay.'

Then an angry man the Duke rade on
    Till he came to bonny Aberdeen,
And there did he see brave Captain Ogilvie
    A-training of his men on the green.

'O woe be to thee, thou Captain Oglivie!
    And an ill death thou shalt dee.
For taking to thee my daughter Jean
    High hangit shalt thou be.'

The Duke has written a broad letter,
    To the King with his own han';
It was to hang Captain Ogilvie
    If ever he hang'd a man.

'I will not hang Captain Ogilvie
    For no lord that I see;
But I'll gar¹ him put off the broad scarlet,
    And put on the single livery.' ²

Now word came to Captain Ogilvie,
    In the chamber where he lay,
To cast off the gold lace and scarlet,
    And put on the single livery.

¹ Make.   ² Private's uniform.

'If this be for bonny Jeanie Gordon,
  This penance I can take wi';
If this be for dear Jeanie Gordon,
  All this and mair will I dree.' [1]

Lady Jeanie had not been married
  A year but only three,
Till she had a babe upon every arm
  And another upon her knee.

'O but I'm weary of wand'rin'!
  O but my fortune is bad!
It sets[2] not the Duke of Gordon's daughter
  To follow a soldier lad.

'O but I'm weary, weary wand'rin'!
  O but I think it lang!
It sets not the Duke of Gordon's daughter
  To follow a single man.'

'O hold thy tongue, Jeanie Gordon,
  O hold they tongue, my lamb!
For once I was a noble captain,
  Now for thy sake a single man.'

But when they came to the Highland hills,
  Cold was the frost and snow;
Lady Jean's shoes they were all torn,
  No farther could she go.

---

[1] Suffer.   [2] Suits.

'Now woe to the hills and the mountains!
  Woe to the wind and the rain!
My feet is sair wi' going barefoot:
  No farther can I gang.

'O were I in the glens o' Foudlen,
  Where hunting I have been,
I would go to bonny Castle Gordon,
  There I'd get hose and sheen!'

When they came to bonny Castle Gordon,
  And standing on the green,
The porter out with a loud loud shout,
  'O here comes our Lady Jean!'—

'You are welcome, bonny Jeanie Gordon,
  You are dear welcome to me;
You are welcome, dear Jeanie Gordon,
  But awa' with your Ogilvie!'

Over-seas now went the Captain,
  As a soldier under command;
But a message soon follow'd after,
  To come home for to heir his land.

'O what does this mean?' says the Captain;
  'Where's my brother's children three?'—
'They are a' o' them dead and buried:
  Come home, pretty Captain Ogilvie!'

'Then hoist up your sail,' says the Captain,
  'And we'll hie back owre the sea;

And I'll gae to bonny Castle Gordon,
    There my dear Jeanie to see.'

He came to bonny Castle Gordon,
    And upon the green stood he:
The porter out with a loud loud shout,
    'Here comes our Captain Ogilvie!'—

'You're welcome, pretty Captain Ogilvie,
    Your furtune's advanced, I hear;
No stranger can come to my castle
    That I do love so dear.'—

'Put up your hat, Duke of Gordon;
    Let it fa' not from your head.
It never set the noble Duke of Gordon
    To bow to a single soldier lad.

'Sir, the last time I was at your Castle,
    You would not let me in;
Now I'm come for my wife and children,
    No friendship else I claim.'

Down the stair Lady Jean came tripping,
    With the saut tear in her e'e;
She had a babe in every arm,
    And another at her knee.

The Captain took her straight in his arms,
    —O a happy man was he!—
Saying, 'Welcome, bonny Jeanie Gordon,
    My Countess o' Cumberland to be!'

TRADITIONAL

The Fair Flower of Northumberland

It was a knight in Scotland born,
  Follow, my love, come over the strand—
Was taken prisoner and left forlorn,
  Even by the good Earl of Northumberland.

Then was he cast in prison strong,
  Follow, my love, come over the strand—
Where he could not walk nor lie along,
  Even by the good Earl of Northumberland.

And as in sorrow thus he lay,
  Follow, my love, come over the strand—
The Earl's sweet daughter walk'd that way,
  And she the faire flower of Northumberland.

And loud to her this knight did crie,
  Follow, my love, come over the strand—
The salt teares standing in his eye,
  And she the faire flower of Northumberland.

'Faire lady,' he said, 'take pity on me,
  Follow, my love, come over the strand—
And let me not in prison dee,
  And you the faire flower of Northumberland.'—

'Faire sir, how should I take pity on thee?
  Follow, my love, come over the strand—
Thou being a foe to our countrie,
  And I the faire flower of Northumberland.'

Faire lady, I am no foe,' he said,
Follow, my love, come over the strand—
'Through thy sweet love here was I stay'd,
For thee, the faire flower of Northumberland.'—

'Why shouldst thou come here for love of me,
Follow, my love, come over the strand—
Having wife and children in thy countrie?
—And I the faire flower of Northumberland.'—

'I swear by the blessed Trinitie,
Follow, my love, come over the strand—
I have no wife nor children, I,
But I'll make you my ladye in faire Scotland.

'I swear by Him that was crown'd with thorn,
Follow, my love, come over the strand—
That I never had wife since the day I was born,
But I live a free lord in faire Scotland.'—

She stole from her father's pillow the key,
Follow, my love, come over the strand—
And soon out of prison she's set him free
To wend with her into faire Scotland.

Likewise much gold she got by sleight,
Follow, my love, come over the strand—
And all to help this forlorne knight
To wend from her father to faire Scotland.

She's led him down to her father's stable,
Follow, my love, come over the strand—
And she's stolen two steeds both wight[1] and able,
To carry them on to faire Scotland.

[1] Strong.

They rode till they came to a water clear,
  Follow, my love, come over the strand—
'Good Sir, how should I follow you here,
  And I the faire flower of Northumberland?

'The water is rough and wonderful steepe,
  Follow, my love, come over the strand—
And on my saddle I shall not keepe,
  And I the faire flower of Northumberland.'—

'Fear not the ford, faire lady,' quoth he,
  Follow, my love, come over the strand—
'For long I cannot stay for thee,
  And thou the faire flower of Northumberland.'

From top to toe all wet was she:
  Follow, my love, come over the strand—
'This have I done for love of thee,
  And I the faire flower of Northumberland.'

They rode till they came to a Scottish moss,
  Follow, my love, come over the strand—
He bade her light off from her father's horse,
  Says, 'Go, get you back to Northumberland.

'For I have a wife and children five,
  Follow, my love, come over the strand—
In Edenborrow they be alive,
  So get thee home to Northumberland.'—

'Have pity on me as I had it on thee!
  Follow, my love, come over the strand—
A cook in your kitchen I will be,
  Even I, the faire flower of Northumberland.

84

'Or take me by the body so meek,
    Follow, my love, come over the strand—
And throw me in the water so deep,
    For I darena go back to Northumberland.'

He turn'd him around and he thought of a plan,
    Follow, my love, come over the strand—
He bought an old horse and he hired an old man
    To carry her back to Northumberland.

When she came thro' her father's ha',
    Follow, my love, come over the strand—
She louted[1] her low among them a',
    She was the faire flower of Northumberland.

Down came her father, he saw her and smiled,
    Follow, my love, come over the strand—
'You arena the first the false Scots have beguiled,
    And ye're aye welcome back to Northumberland

TRADITIONAL

[1] Bowed.

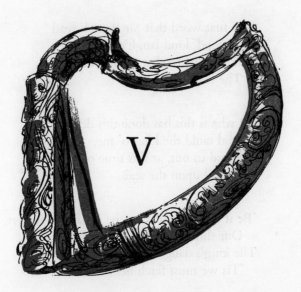

V

Sir Patrick Spens

THE king sits in Dunfermline town
 Drinking the blude-red wine,
'O whare will I get a skeely[1] skipper
 To sail this new ship o' mine?'

O up and spak an eldern knight,
 Sat at the king's right knee;
'Sir Patrick Spens is the best sailor
 That ever sailed the sea.'

Our king has written a braid[2] letter,
 And seal'd it with his hand,
And sent it to Sir Patrick Spens,
 Was walking on the strand.

 [1] Skilful.   [2] Broad, plain.

The first word that Sir Patrick read
   So loud, loud laugh'd he;
The next word that Sir Patrick read
   The tear blinded his e'e.

'O wha is this has done this deed
   And tauld the king o' me,
To send us out, at this time o' year,
   To sail upon the sea?

'Be it wind, be it weet, be it hail, be it sleet,
   Our ship must sail the faem;
The king's daughter o' Noroway,
   'Tis we must fetch her hame.'

They hadna been a week, a week,
   In Noroway but twae,
When that the lords o' Noroway
   Began aloud to say:

'Ye Scottish men spend a' our king's gowd,
   And a' our quennis fee.'
'Ye lee, ye lee, ye leears loud,
   Fu' loud I hear ye lee!

'For I brought as much o' the white monie
   As gane[1] my men and me,
And a half-fou[2] o' the gude red gowd,
   Out ower the sea with me.

[1] Suffices.   [2] Half-bushel.

'Mak' ready, mak' ready, my merry men a'!
   Our gude ship sails the morn.'
'Now ever alack, my master dear,
   I fear a deadly storm.

'I saw the new moon late yestreen
   Wi' the auld moon in her arm;
And if we gang to sea, master,
   I fear we'll come to harm.'

They hadna sail'd a league, a league,
   A league but barely three,
When the lift[1] grew dark, and the wind blew loud,
   And gurly[2] grew the sea.

The ankers brak, and the topmast lap,[3]
   It was sic a deadly storm:
And the waves cam owre the broken ship
   Till a' her sides were torn.

   [1] Sky.   [2] Rough.   [3] Cracked.

They fetch'd a web o' the silken claith,[1]
   Another o' the twine,[2]
And they wapp'd[3] them round that gude ship's side,
   But still the sea came in.

O laith,[4] laith were our gude Scots lords
   To wet their cork-heel'd shoon;
But lang or a' the play was play'd
   They wat their hats aboon.[5]

And mony was the feather bed
   That flatter'd[6] on the faem;
And mony was the gude lord's son
   That never mair cam hame.

O lang, lang may the ladies sit,
   Wi' their fans into their hand,
Before they see Sir Patrick Spens
   Come sailing to the strand!

And lang, lang may the maidens sit
   Wi' their gowd kames[7] in their hair,
A-waiting for their ain dear loves!
   For them they'll see nae mair.

Half-owre,[8] half-owre to Aberdour,
   'Tis fifty fathoms deep;
And there lies gude Sir Patrick Spens,
   Wi' the Scots lords at his feet!

TRADITIONAL

[1] Cloth.   [2] Sacking.   [3] Packed.   [4] Loath.
[5] Above.   [6] Floated.   [7] Golden combs.   [8] Half way over.

A Ballad of Agincourt

FAIR stood the wind for France
 When we our sails advance,
Nor now to prove our chance
 Longer will tarry;
But putting to the main,
At Caux, the mouth of Seine,
With all his martial train
 Landed King Harry.

And taking many a fort,
Furnish'd in warlike sort,
Marcheth tow'rds Agincourt
 In happy hour;
Skirmishing day by day
With those that stopp'd his way.
Where the French gen'ral lay
 With all his power.

Which, in his height of pride,
King Henry to deride,
His ransom to provide
 To the King sending;
Which he neglects the while
As from a nation vile,
Yet with an angry smile
 Their fall portending.

And turning to his men,
Quoth our brave Henry then,
'Though they to one be ten
   Be not amazèd:
Yet have we well begun;
Battles so bravely won
Have ever to the sun
   By fame been raisèd.

'And for myself (quoth he)
This my full rest shall be:
England ne'er mourn for me
   Nor more esteem me:
Victor I will remain
Or on this earth lie slain,
Never shall she sustain
   Loss to redeem me.

'Poitiers and Cressy tell
When most their pride did swell,
Under our swords they fell:
   No less our skill is
Than when our grandsire great,
Claiming the regal seat,
By many a warlike feat
   Lopp'd the French lilies.'

The Duke of York so dread
The eager vaward[1] led;
With the main Henry sped
   Among his henchmen.

[1] Vanguard.

Excester had the rear,
A braver man not there;
O Lord, how hot they were
   On the false Frenchmen!

They now to fight are gone,
Armour on armour shone,
Drum now to drum did groan,
   To hear was wonder.
That with the cries they make
The very earth did shake:
Trumpet to trumpet spake,
   Thunder to thunder.

Well it thine age became,
O noble Erpingham,
Which didst the signal aim
   To our hid forces!
When from a meadow by,
Like a storm suddenly
The English archery
   Stuck the French horses.

With Spanish yew so strong
Arrows a cloth-yard long
That like to serpents stung,
   Piercing the weather;
None from his fellow starts,
But playing manly parts,
And like true English hearts
   Stuck close together.

When down their bows they threw,
And forth their bilbos[1] drew,
And on the French they flew,
  Not one was tardy;
Arms were from shoulders sent,
Scalps to the teeth were rent,
Down the French peasants went—
  Our men were hardy.

This while our noble king,
His broadsword brandishing,
Down the French host did ding[2]
  As to o'erwhelm it;
And many a deep wound lent,
His arms with blood besprent,[3]
And many a cruel dent
  Bruisèd his helmet.

Gloster, that duke so good,
Next of the royal blood,
For famous England stood
  With his brave brother;
Clarence, in steel so bright,
Though but a maiden knight,
Yet in that furious fight
  Scarce such another.

Warwick in blood did wade,
Oxford the foe invade,
And cruel slaughter made
  Still as they ran up;

[1] Swords. [2] Knock. [3] Spattered.

94

Suffolk his axe did ply,
Beaumont and Willoughby
Bare them right doughtily,
  Ferrers and Fanhope.

Upon Saint Crispin's Day
Fought was this noble fray,
Which fame did not delay
  To England to carry.
O when shall English men
With such acts fill a pen?
Or England breed again
  Such a King Harry?

MICHAEL DRAYTON

Song on the Victory of Agincourt

OUR King went forth to Normandy,
With grace and might of chivalry;
The God for him wrought marv'lously,
Wherefore England may call and cry
  Deo Gratias.[1]

He set a siege, the sooth for to say,
To Harfleur town with royal array;
That town he won, and made a fray,
That France shall rue till Domesday.
  Deo Gratias.

[1] Thanks be to God.

Then went our King, with all his host,
Through France for all the Frenchman's boast:
He spared for dread of least nor most,
Until he came to Agincourt coast.
   Deo Gratias.

Then forsooth that Knight comely,
In Agincourt field he fought manly:
Through grace of God most mighty,
He had both the field and the victory.
   Deo Gratias.

Their dukes and earls, lord and baron,
Were taken and slain and that well soon:
And some were led into London,
With joy and mirth and great renown.
   Deo Gratias.

The gracious God now save our King,
His people and all his well-willing:
Give him good life and good ending,
That we with mirth may safely sing.
   Deo Gratias.

The Bonny Earl of Murray

YE Highlands and ye Lawlands,
 O where hae ye been?
They hae slain the Earl of Murray,
 And hae laid him on the green.

Now wae be to thee, Huntley!
 And whairfore did ye sae!
I bade you bring him wi' you,
 But forbade you him to slay.

He was a braw gallant,
 And he rid at the ring;
And the bonny Earl of Murray,
 O he might hae been a king!

He was a braw gallant,
 And he play'd at the ba';
And the bonny Earl of Murray
 Was the flower amang them a'!

He was a braw gallant,
 And he play'd at the gluve;
And the bonny Earl of Murray,
 O he was the Queen's luve!

O lang will his Lady
 Look owre the Castle Downe,
Ere she see the Earl of Murray
 Come sounding through the town!

TRADITIONAL

BOSTON STUMP
from an early 19th-century engraving

The High Tide on the Coast of Lincolnshire

(1571)

THE old mayor climbed the belfry tower,
  The ringers ran by two, by three;
'Pull, if ye never pulled before;
  Good ringers, pull your best,' quoth he.
'Play uppe, play uppe, O Boston bells!
Ply all your changes, all your swells,
  Play uppe, "The Brides of Enderby".'

Men say it was a stolen tyde—
  The Lord that sent it, He knows all;
But in myne ears doth still abide
  The message that the bells let fall:
And there was nought of strange, beside
The flights of mews and peewits pied
  By millions crouched on the old sea wall.

I sat and spun within the doore,
  My thread brake off, I raised myne eyes;
The level sun, like ruddy ore,
  Lay sinking in the barren skies,
And dark against day's golden death
She moved where Lindis wandereth,
My sonne's faire wife, Elizabeth.

'Cusha! Cusha! Cusha!' calling,
Ere the early dews were falling,
Farre away I heard her song.
'Cusha! Cusha!' all along
Where the reedy Lindis floweth,
      Floweth, floweth;
From the meads where melick groweth
Faintly came her milking song—

'Cusha! Cusha! Cusha!' calling,
'For the dews will soone be falling;
Leave your meadow grasses mellow,
      Mellow, mellow,
Quit your cowslips, cowslips yellow;
Come uppe Whitefoot, come uppe Lightfoot,
Quit the stalks of parsley hollow,
      Hollow, hollow;

'Come uppe Jetty, rise and follow,
From the clovers lift your head;
Come uppe Whitefoot, come uppe Lightfoot,
Come uppe Jetty, rise and follow,
Jetty, to the milking shed.'

If it be long, ay, long ago,
    When I beginne to think howe long,
Againe I hear the Lindis flow,
    Swift as an arrowe, sharpe and strong;
And all the aire, it seemeth mee,
Bin full of floating bells (sayth shee),
That ring the tune of Enderby.

Alle fresh the level pasture lay
   And not a shadowe mote be seene,
Save where full fyve good miles away
   The steeple towered from out the greene;
And lo! the great bell farre and wide
Was heard in all the country side
That Saturday at eventide.

The swanherds where their sedges are
   Moved on in sunset's golden breath,
The shepherde lads I heard afarre,
   And my sonne's wife, Elizabeth;
Till floating o'er the grassy sea
Came downe that kindly message free,
The 'Brides of Mavis Enderby'.

Then some looked uppe into the sky,
   And all along where Lindis flows
To where the goodly vessels lie,
   And where the lordly steeple shows,
They sayde, 'And why should this thing be?
What danger lowers by land or sea?
They ring the tune of Enderby!

'For evil news from Mablethorpe,
   Of pyrate galleys warping downe;
For shippes ashore beyond the scorpe,
   They have not spared to wake the towne:
But while the west bin red to see,
And storms be none, and pyrates flee,
Why ring "The Brides of Enderby"?'

I looked without, and lo! my sonne
   Came riding downe with might and main:
He raised a shout as he drew on,
   Till all the welkin rang again,
'Elizabeth! Elizabeth!'
(A sweeter woman ne'er drew breath
Than my sonne's wife, Elizabeth.)

'The olde sea wall (he cried) is downe,
   The rising tide comes on apace,
And boats adrift in yonder towne
   Go sailing uppe the market-place.'
He shook as one that looks on death:
'God save you, mother!' straight he saith;
'Where is my wife, Elizabeth?'

'Good sonne, where Lindis winds away,
   With her two bairns I marked her long;
And ere yon bells beganne to play
   Afar I heard her milking-song.'
He looked across the grassy lea,
To right, to left, 'Ho Enderby!'
They rang 'The Brides of Enderby'!

With that he cried and beat his breast;
   For lo! along the river's bed
A mighty eygre[1] reared his crest,
   And uppe the Lindis raging sped.
It swept with thunderous noises loud;
Shaped like a curling snow-white cloud,
Or like a demon in a shroud.

[1] Tidal wave.

And rearing Lindis backward pressed
    Shook all her trembling bankes amaine,
Then madly at the eygre's breast
    Flung uppe her weltering walls again.
Then bankes came down with ruin and rout—
Then beaten foam flew round about—
Then all the mighty floods were out.

So farre, so fast the eygre drave,
    The heart had hardly time to beat,
Before a shallow seething wave
    Sobbed in the grasses at our feet:
The feet had hardly time to flee
Before it brake against the knee,
And all the world was in the sea.

Upon the roofe we sate that night,
    The noise of bells went sweeping by;
I marked the lofty beacon light
    Stream from the church tower, red and high—
A lurid mark and dread to see;
And awsome bells they were to me,
That in the dark rang 'Enderby'.

They rang the sailor lads to guide
    From roofe to roofe who fearless rowed;
And I—my sonne was at my side,
    And yet the ruddy beacon glowed;
And yet he moaned beneath his breath,
'O come in life, or come in death!
O lost! my love, Elizabeth.'

And didst thou visit him no more?
   Thou didst, thou didst, my daughter deare
The waters laid thee at his doore,
   Ere yet the early dawn was clear.
Thy pretty bairns in fast embrace,
The lifted sun shone on thy face,
Downe drifted to thy dwelling-place.

That flow strewed wrecks about the grass,
   That ebbe swept out the flocks to sea;
A fatal ebbe and flow, alas!
   To manye more than myne and mee:
But each will mourn his own (she saith),
And sweeter woman ne'er drew breath
Than my sonne's wife, Elizabeth.

I shall never hear her more
By the reedy Lindis shore,
'Cusha! Cusha! Cusha!' calling
Ere the early dews be falling;
I shall never hear her song,
'Cusha! Cusha!' all along
Where the sunny Lindis floweth,
    Goeth, floweth;
From the meads where melick groweth
When the water winding down,
Onward floweth to the town.

I shall never see her more
Where the reeds and rushes quiver,
    Shiver, quiver;
Stand beside the sobbing river,
Sobbing, throbbing in its falling
To the sandy lonesome shore;
I shall never hear her calling,
'Leave your meadow grasses mellow,
    Mellow, mellow;
Quit your cowslips, cowslips yellow;
Come uppe Whitefoot, come uppe Lightfoot;
Quit your pipes of parsley hollow,
    Hollow, hollow;
Come uppe Lightfoot, rise and follow;
    Lightfoot, Whitefoot,
From your clovers lift the head;
Come uppe Jetty, follow, follow,
Jetty, to the milking shed.'

JEAN INGELOW

After Blenheim

It was a summer evening,
  Old Kaspar's work was done,
And he before his cottage door
  Was sitting in the sun;
And by him sported on the green
His little grandchild Wilhelmine.

She saw her brother Peterkin
  Roll something large and round
Which he beside the rivulet
  In playing there had found;
He came to ask what he had found
That was so large and smooth and round.

Old Kaspar took it from the boy
  Who stood expectant by;
And then the old man shook his head,
  And with a natural sigh,
' 'Tis some poor fellow's skull,' said he,
'Who fell in the great victory.

'I find them in the garden,
  For there's many here about;
And often when I go to plough
  The ploughshare turns them out.
For many thousand men,' said he,
'Were slain in that great victory.'

ROBERT SOUTHEY

The Loss of the 'Royal George'

TOLL for the brave!
  The brave that are no more:
All sunk beneath the wave
  Fast by their native shore!

Eight hundred of the brave,
  Whose courage well was tried,
Had made the vessel heel,
  And laid her on her side.

A land-breeze shook the shrouds,
  And she was overset;
Down went the *Royal George*,
  With all her crew complete.

Toll for the brave!
  Brave Kempenfelt is gone;
His last sea-fight is fought,
  His work of glory done.

It was not in the battle;
  No tempest gave the shock;
She sprang no fatal leak;
  She ran upon no rock.

His sword was in its sheath,
  His fingers held the pen,
When Kempenfelt went down
  With twice four hundred men.

National Maritime Museum

THE LOSS OF THE ROYAL GEORGE
lithograph after W. Mitchell, published 1839

Weigh the vessel up
  Once dreaded by our foes!
And mingle with our cup
  The tear that England owes.

Her timbers yet are sound,
  And she may float again
Full charged with England's thunder,
  And plough the distant main.

But Kempenfelt is gone,
  His victories are o'er;
And he and his eight hundred
  Shall plough the wave no more.

WILLIAM COWPER

The Burial of Sir John Moore
at Corunna

NOT a drum was heard, not a funeral note,
  As his corpse to the rampart we hurried;
Not a soldier discharged his farewell shot,
  O'er the grave where our hero we buried.

We buried him darkly, at dead of night,
  The sods with our bayonets turning;
By the struggling moonbeam's misty light,
  And the lantern dimly burning.

No useless coffin enclosed his breast,
    Not in sheet nor in shroud we wound him;
But he lay like a warrior taking his rest,
    With his martial cloak around him.

Few and short were the prayers we said,
    And we spoke not a word of sorrow;
But we steadfastly gazed on the face that was dead,
    And we bitterly thought of the morrow.

We thought, as we hollowed his narrow bed,
    And smoothed down his lonely pillow,
That the foe and the stranger would tread o'er his head,
    And we far away on the billow!

Lightly they'll talk of the spirit that's gone,
    And o'er his cold ashes upbraid him;—
But little he'll reck, if they let him sleep on,
    In the grave where a Briton has laid him.

But half of our heavy task was done
    When the clock struck the hour for retiring;
And we heard the distant and random gun
    That the foe was sullenly firing.

Slowly and sadly we laid him down,
    From the field of his fame fresh and gory;
We carved not a line, and we raised not a stone—
    But we left him alone with his glory.

CHARLES WOLFE

VI

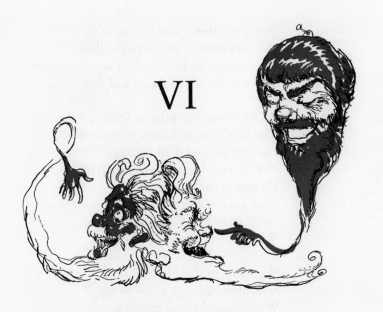

The War-Song of Dinas Vawr

THE mountain sheep are sweeter,
But the valley sheep are fatter;
We therefore deemed it meeter
To carry off the latter.
We made an expedition;
We met a host and quelled it;
We forced a strong position,
And killed the men who held it.

On Dyfed's richest valley,
Where herds of kine were browsing,
We made a mighty sally,
To furnish our carousing.

Fierce warriors rushed to meet us;
We met them, and o'erthrew them:
They struggled hard to beat us;
But we conquered them, and slew them.

As we drove our prize at leisure,
The king marched forth to catch us:
His rage surpassed all measure,
But his people could not match us.
He fled to his hall-pillars;
And, ere our force we led off,
Some sacked his house and cellars,
While others cut his head off.

We there, in strife bewild'ring,
Spilt blood enough to swim in:
We orphaned many children,
And widowed many women.
The eagles and the ravens
We glutted with our foemen,
The heroes and the cravens,
The spearmen and the bowmen.

We brought away from battle,
And much their land bemoaned them,
Two thousand head of cattle,
And the head of him who owned them:
Ednyfed, King of Dyfed,
His head was borne before us;
His wine and beasts supplied our feasts,
And his overthrow, our chorus.

THOMAS LOVE PEACOCK

The Mole-Catcher

A MOLE-catcher am I, and that is my trade,
I potters about wi' my spunt and my spade,
    On a moon-shiny night, O! 'tis my delight,
      A-catching o' moles.

The traps that I set for the mole in his run,
There's never a night, sirs, but I catches one.
    On a moon-shiny night, . . .

Along of the lanes as by night-time I go,
There's things that I see, as the folks don't know,
    On a moon-shiny night, . . .

There's frolic and lark in the field and the park,
For others than moles will be out in the dark,
    On a moon-shiny night, . . .

The maiden by day that's too modest to speak
Is gadding abroad, by the night all the week,
    On a moon-shiny night, . . .

The 'prentice who should be a lying in bed
Is rambling over the meadows instead,
    On a moon-shiny night, . . .

I light on the poacher wi' sniggle and snare,
But that I'll not peach he is surely aware,
    On a moon-shiny night, . . .

The doctor and lawyer as drunk as a dog,
Are wallowing into a ditch or a bog,
   On a moon-shiny night, . . .

There's many a sight; and there's many a sound
Wot maketh me laugh as I'm making my round,
   On a moon-shiny night, . . .

But nothing I sez for I'm mum as a bell,
You certainly know that no tales will I tell,
   On a moon-shiny night, O! 'tis my delight,
      A-catching o' moles
        Not human souls.

ANONYMOUS

Epitaph on a Dentist

STRANGER, approach this spot with gravity;
John Brown is filling his last cavity.

ANONYMOUS

Queer Things

VERY, very queer things have been happening to me
    In some of the places where I've been.
I went to the pillar-box this morning with a letter
    And a hand came out and took it in.

'So I took my newspaper and went into the park,
    And looked round to see no one was near,
When a voice right out of the middle of the paper
    Started reading the news bold and clear!

'When I got home again, I thought I'd have
    A glass of spirits to steady myself;
And I take my bible oath, but that bottle and glass
    Came a-hopping down off the shelf.

'No, no, I says, I'd better take no spirits,
    And I sat down to have a cup of tea;
And blowed if my old pair of carpet-slippers
    Didn't walk across the carpet to me!

'So I took my newspaper and went into the park,
    And looked round to see no one was near,
When a voice right out of the middle of the paper
    Started reading the news bold and clear!

'Well, I guess there's some magician out to help me,
    So perhaps there's no need for alarm;
And if I manage not to anger him,
    Why should he do me any harm?'

JAMES REEVES

The Dong with a Luminous Nose

WHEN awful darkness and silence reign
Over the great Gromboolian plain,
  Through the long, long wintry nights;—
    When the angry breakers roar
    As they beat on the rocky shore;—
When Storm-clouds brood on the towering heights
  Of the Hills of the Chankly Bore:—

Then, through the vast and gloomy dark,
There moves what seems a fiery spark,
  A lonely spark with silvery rays
    Piercing the coal-black night,—
    A meteor strange and bright;—
Hither and thither the vision strays,
    A single lurid light.

Slowly it wanders,—pauses,—creeps,—
Anon it sparkles,—flashes and leaps;
And ever as onward it gleaming goes
A light on the Bong-tree stems it throws.

And those who watch at that midnight hour
From Hall or Terrace, or lofty Tower,
Cry, as the wild light passes along,—
    'The Dong!—the Dong!
  'The wandering Dong through the forest goes!
    'The Dong!—the Dong!
  'The Dong with a luminous Nose!'

Long years ago
   The Dong was happy and gay,
Till he fell in love with a Jumbly Girl
   Who came to those shores one day.
For the Jumblies came in a Sieve, they did,—
Landing at eve near the Zemmery Fidd
      Where the Oblong Oysters grow,
   And the rocks are smooth and gray.
And all the woods and valleys rang
With the Chorus they daily and nightly sang,—
      'Far and few, far and few,
      Are the lands where the Jumblies live;
      Their heads are green, and their hands are blue,
      And they went to sea in a sieve.'

Happily, happily passed those days!
   While the cheerful Jumblies staid;
   They danced in circles all night long,
   To the plaintive pipe of the lively Dong,
      In moonlight, shine or shade.
For day and night he was always there
By the side of the Jumbly Girl so fair,
With her sky-blue hands, and her sea-green hair.

Till the morning came of that hateful day
When the Jumblies sailed in their sieve away,
And the Dong was left on the cruel shore
Gazing—gazing for evermore,—
Ever keeping his weary eyes on
That pea-green sail on the far horizon,—
Singing the Jumbly Chorus still
As he sate all day on the grassy hill,—

'Far and few, far and few,
Are the lands where the Jumblies live;
Their heads are green, and their hands are blue,
And they went to sea in a sieve.'

But when the sun was low in the West,
    The Dong arose and said,—
    'What little sense I once possessed
    Has quite gone out of my head!'
And since that day he wanders still
By lake and forest, marsh and hill,
Singing—'O somewhere, in valley or plain
Might I find my Jumbly Girl again!
For ever I'll seek by lake and shore
Till I find my Jumbly Girl once more!'

    Playing a pipe with silvery squeaks,
    Since then his Jumbly Girl he seeks.
    And because by night he could not see,
    He gathered the bark of the Twangum Tree
        On the flowery plain that grows.
        And he wove him a wondrous Nose,—
    A Nose as strange as a Nose could be!
Of vast proportions and painted red,
And tied with cords to the back of his head.
    —In a hollow rounded space it ended
    With a luminous lamp within suspended,
        All fenced about
        With a bandage stout
        To prevent the wind from blowing it out;—
And with holes all round to send the light,
In gleaming rays on the dismal night.

And now each night, and all night long,
Over those plains still roams the Dong;
And above the wail of the Chimp and Snipe
You may hear the squeak of his plaintive pipe
While ever he seeks, but seeks in vain
To meet with his Jumbly Girl again;
Lonely and wild—all night he goes.—
The Dong with a luminous Nose.
And all who watch at the midnight hour,
From Hall or Terrace, or lofty Tower,
Cry, as they trace the Meteor bright,
Moving along through the dreary night,—
  'This is the hour when forth he goes,
  The Dong with a luminous Nose!
  Yonder—over the plain he goes;
    He goes!
    He goes;
  The Dong with a luminous Nose!'

EDWARD LEAR

Hope

WOLF has turned to house-dog,
Tiger-cat to kitty,
Timid horse to charger,
Or drayhorse in the city;
Stones are raised to steeples,
Iron floats at sea,
Cannibals grow Christians—
There's hope for you and me!

E. L. M. KING

The Big Rock Candy Mountains

(American Tramps' Song)

ONE evenin' as the sun went down
And the jungle fire was burnin',
Down the track came a hobo hikin'
And he said, 'Boys, I'm not turnin',
I'm headed fur a land that's far away
Beside the crystal fountains,
So come with me, we'll all go see
The Big Rock Candy Mountains.

'In the Big Rock Candy Mountains
There's a land that's fair and bright,
Where the hand-outs grow on bushes
And you sleep out every night,
Where the boxcars[1] are all empty,
And the sun shines every day
On the birds and the bees and the cigarette trees,
And the lemonade springs where the bluebird sings,
In the Big Rock Candy Mountains.

In the Big Rock Candy Mountains
All the cops have wooden legs,
The bulldogs all have rubber teeth,
And the hens lay soft-boiled eggs,
The farmers' trees are full of fruit,
And the barns are full of hay,
Oh, I'm bound to go where there ain't no snow,
Where the rain don't pour, the wind don't blow,
In the Big Rock Candy Mountains.

[1] Covered goods wagons.

In the Big Rock Candy Mountains
You never change your socks,
And the little streams of alcohol
Come tricklin' down the rocks.
There the brakemen[1] have to tip their hats
And the railroad bulls[2] are blind.
There's a lake of stew and of whisky too,
You can paddle all around 'em in a big canoe,
In the Big Rock Candy Mountains.

In the Big Rock Candy Mountains
All the jails are made of tin,
And you can bust right out again
As soon as you are in.
There ain't no short-handled shovels,
No axes, saws or picks.
I'm going to stay where you sleep all day,
Where they hung the Turk that invented work,
In the Big Rock Candy Mountains.

TRADITIONAL

[1] Guards.   [2] Policemen.

Our Village

(By a Villager)

OUR village, that's to say not Miss Mitford's[1] village, but our
  village of Bullock Smithy,
Is come into by an avenue of trees, three oak pollards, two
  elders, and a withy;
And in the middle, there's a green of about not exceeding an
  acre and a half;
It's common to all, and fed off by nineteen cows, six ponies, three
  horses, five asses, two foals, seven pigs, and a calf!
Besides a pond in the middle, as is held by a similar sort of
  common law lease,
And contains twenty ducks, six drakes, three ganders, two dead
  dogs, four drown'd kittens, and twelve geese.
Of course the green's cropt very close, and does famous for
  bowling when the little village boys play at cricket;
Only some horse, or pig, or cow, or great jackass, is sure to come
  and stand right before the wicket.
There's fifty-five private houses, let alone barns and workshops,
  and pigstyes, and poultry huts, and such-like sheds;
With plenty of public-houses—two Foxes, one Green Man, three
  Bunch of Grapes, one Crown, and six King's Heads.
The Green Man is reckon'd the best, as the only one that for love
  or money can raise
A postilion, a blue jacket, two deplorable lame white horses, and
  a ramshackled 'neat postchaise'.
There's one parish church for all the people, whatsoever may be
  their ranks in life or their degrees,
Except one very damp, small, dark, freezing-cold, little Methodist
  chapel of Ease;

[1] Miss Mitford was the early Victorian authoress of a book of idealized
pictures of rural life entitled *Our Village*.

And close by the church-yard there's a stone-mason's yard, that when the time is seasonable
Will furnish with afflictions sore and marble urns and cherabims very low and reasonable.
There's a cage, comfortable enough; I've been in it with old Jack Jeffrey and Tom Pike;
For the Green Man next door will send you in ale, gin, or any thing else you like.
I can't speak of the stocks, as nothing remains of them but the upright post;
But the pound is kept in repairs for the sake of Cob's horse, as is always there almost.
There's a smithy of course, where that queer sort of a chap in his way, Old Joe Bradley,
Perpetually hammers and stammers, for he stutters and shoes horses very badly.
There's a shop of all sorts, that sells every thing, kept by the widow of Mr Task;
But when you go there it's ten to one she's out of every thing you ask.
You'll know her house by the swarm of boys, like flies, about the old sugary cask:
There are six empty houses, and not so well paper'd inside as out,
For bill-stickers won't beware, but sticks notices of sales and election placards all about.
That's the Doctor's with a green door, where the garden pots in the windows is seen;
A weakly monthly rose that don't blow, and a dead geranium, and a tea-plant with five black leaves and one green.
As for hollyoaks at the cottage doors, and honeysuckles and jasmines, you may go and whistle;
But the Tailor's front garden grows two cabbages, a dock, a ha'porth of pennyroyal, two dandelions, and a thistle.

There are three small orchards—Mr Busby's the schoolmaster's is the chief—
With two pear-trees that don't bear; one plum and an apple, that every year is stripped by a thief.
There's another small day-school too, kept by the respectable Mrs Gaby.
A select establishment, for six little boys and one big, and four little girls and a baby;
There's a rectory, with pointed gables and strange odd chimneys that never smokes,
For the rector don't live on his living like other Christian sort of folks;
There's a barber's, once a-week well filled with rough black-bearded, shock-headed churls,
And a window with two feminine men's heads, and two masculine ladies in false curls;
There's a butcher's, and a carpenter's, and a plumber's, and a small green-grocer's, and a baker,
But he won't bake on a Sunday, and there's a sexton that's a coal-merchant besides, and an undertaker;
And a toy-shop, but not a whole one, for a village can't compare with the London shops;
One window sells drums, dolls, kites, carts, bats, Clout's balls, and the other sells malt and hops.
And Mrs Brown, in domestic economy not to be a bit behind her betters,
Lets her house to a milliner, a watchmaker, a rat-catcher, a cobbler, lives in it herself, and it's the post-office for letters.
Now I've gone through all the village—ay, from end to end, save and except one more house,
But I haven't come to that—and I hope I never shall—and that's the Village Poor House.

THOMAS HOOD

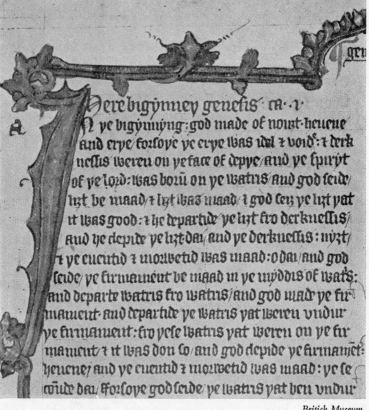

IN THE BEGINNING
from a medieval Bible manuscript

VII

In the Beginning

(from *The Book of Genesis*)

IN the beginning God created the heaven and the earth. And the earth was without form, and void; and darkness was upon the face of the deep. And the Spirit of God moved upon the face of the waters. And God said, Let there be light: and there was light. And God saw the light, that it was good: and God divided the light from the darkness. And God called the light Day, and the darkness he called Night. And the evening and the morning were the first day.

The Earth is the Lord's

(Psalm 24)

THE earth is the Lord's, and the fullness thereof;
The world, and they that dwell therein.
For he hath founded it upon the seas,
And established it upon the floods.
　　Who shall ascend into the hill of the Lord?
　　Or who shall stand in his holy place?
　　　He that hath clean hands, and a pure heart;
　　Who hath not lifted up his soul unto vanity, nor sworn
　　　deceitfully.
　　He shall receive the blessing from the Lord,
　　And righteousness from the God of his salvation.
　　This is the generation of them that seek him,
　　That seek thy face, O Jacob.

　　Lift up your heads, O ye gates;
　　And be ye lift up, ye everlasting doors;
　　And the King of glory shall come in.
Who is this King of glory?
　　　The Lord strong and mighty,
　　　The Lord mighty in battle.
　　Lift up your heads, O ye gates;
　　Even lift them up, ye everlasting doors;
　　And the King of glory shall come in.
Who is this King of glory?
　　　The Lord of hosts,
　　　He is the King of glory.

The War Horse

(from *The Book of Job*)

HAST thou given the horse strength?
Hast thou clothed his neck with thunder?
Canst thou make him afraid as a grasshopper?
The glory of his nostrils is terrible.

He paweth in the valley, and rejoiceth in his strength:
He goeth on to meet the armed men.
He mocketh at fear, and is not affrighted;
Neither turneth he back from the sword.
The quiver rattleth against him,
The glittering spear and the shield.
He swalloweth the ground with fierceness and rage:
Neither believeth he that it is the sound of the trumpet.

He saith among the trumpets, Ha, ha;
And he smelleth the battle afar off,
The thunder of the captains, and the shouting.

Lord Randal

'O WHERE hae ye been, Lord Randal, my son?
O where hae ye been, my handsome young man?'
'I hae been to the wild wood; mother, make my bed soon,
For I'm weary wi' hunting, and fain wad lie down.'

'Where gat ye your dinner, Lord Randal, my son?
Where gat ye your dinner, my handsome young man?'
'I dined wi' my true-love; mother, make my bed soon,
For I'm weary wi' hunting, and fain wad lie down.'

'What gat ye to your dinner, Lord Randal, my son?
What gat ye to your dinner, my handsome young man?'
'I gat eels boiled in broth; mother, make my bed soon,
For I'm weary wi' hunting, and fain wad lie down.'

'And wha gat your leavings, Lord Randal, my son?
And wha gat your leavings, my handsome young man?'
'My hawks and my hounds; mother, make my bed soon,
For I'm weary wi' hunting, and fain wad lie down.'

'What became of your bloodhounds, Lord Randal, my son?
What became of your bloodhounds, my handsome young
    man?'
'O they swelled and they died; mother, make my bed soon,
For I'm weary wi' hunting, and fain wad lie down.'

'O I fear ye are poisoned, Lord Randal, my son!
O I fear ye are poisoned, my handsome young man!'
'O yes! I am poisoned; mother, make my bed soon,
For I'm sick at the heart and I fain wad lie down.'

TRADITIONAL

The Golden Journey to Samarkand

(EPILOGUE. From *Hassan*)

At the Gate of the Sun, Bagdad, in olden time

THE MERCHANTS (*together*)

AWAY, for we are ready to a man!
　　Our camels sniff the evening and are glad.
Lead on, O Master of the Caravan:
　　Lead on the Merchant-Princes of Bagdad.

THE CHIEF DRAPER

Have we not Indian carpets dark as wine,
　　Turbans and sashes, gowns and bows and veils,
And broideries of intricate design,
　　And printed hangings in enormous bales?

THE CHIEF GROCER

We have rose-candy, we have spikenard,
　　Mastic and terebinth and oil and spice,
And such sweet jams meticulously jarred
　　As God's own Prophet eats in Paradise.

THE PRINCIPAL JEWS

And we have manuscripts in peacock styles
    By Ali of Damascus; we have swords
Engraved with storks and apes and crocodiles,
    And heavy beaten necklaces, for Lords.

THE MASTER OF THE CARAVAN

But you are nothing but a lot of Jews.

THE PRINCIPAL JEWS

Sir, even dogs have daylight, and we pay.

THE MASTER OF THE CARAVAN

But who are ye in rags and rotten shoes,
    You dirty-bearded, blocking up the way?

THE PILGRIMS

We are the Pilgrims, master; we shall go
    Always a little further: it may be
Beyond that last blue mountain barred with snow,
    Across that angry or that glimmering sea,
White on a throne or guarded in a cave
    There lives a prophet who can understand
Why men are born: but surely we are brave,
    Who make the Golden Journey to Samarkand.

THE CHIEF MERCHANT

We gnaw the nail of hurry. Master, away!

One of the Women

O turn your eyes to where your children stand.
Is not Bagdad the beautiful? O stay!

The Merchants (*in chorus*)

We take the Golden Road to Samarkand.

An Old Man

Have you not girls and garlands in your homes,
    Eunuchs and Syrian boys at your command?
Seek not excess: God hateth him who roams!

The Merchants (*in chorus*)

We make the Golden Journey to Samarkand.

A Pilgrim with a Beautiful Voice

Sweet to ride forth at evening from the wells
    When shadows pass gigantic on the sand,
And softly through the silence beat the bells
    Along the Golden Road to Samarkand.

A Merchant

We travel not for trafficking alone:
    By hotter winds our fiery hearts are fanned:
For lust of knowing what should not be known
    We make the Golden Journey to Samarkand.

The Master of the Caravan

Open the gate, O watchman of the night!

The Watchman

Ho, travellers, I open. For what land
Leave you the dim-moon city of delight?

The Merchants (*with a shout*)

We make the Golden Journey to Samarkand.
     (*The Caravan passes through the gate*)

The Watchman (*consoling the women*)

What should ye, ladies? It was ever thus.
     Men are unwise and curiously planned.

A Woman

They have their dreams, and do not think of us.

Voices of the Caravan (*in the distance, singing*)

We make the Golden Journey to Samarkand.
                                    JAMES ELROY FLECKER

The Congo

I. *Their Basic Savagery*

FAT black bucks in a wine-barrel room,
Barrel-house kings, with feet unstable,
Sagged and reeled and pounded on the table,
Pounded on the table,
Beat an empty barrel with the handle of a broom,
Hard as they were able,
Boom, boom, BOOM,
With a silk umbrella and the handle of a broom,
Boomlay, boomlay, boomlay, BOOM.
THEN I had religion, THEN I had a vision.
I could not turn from their revel in derision.
THEN I SAW THE CONGO, CREEPING THROUGH THE
BLACK,
CUTTING THROUGH THE FOREST WITH A GOLDEN
TRACK.
Then along that riverbank
A thousand miles
Tattooed cannibals danced in files;
Then I heard the boom of the blood-lust song
And a thigh-bone beating on a tin-pan gong.
And 'BLOOD' screamed the whistles and the fifes
of the warriors,
'BLOOD' screamed the skull-faced lean witch-
doctors.
'Whirl ye the deadly voo-doo rattle,
Harry the uplands,
Steal all the cattle,
Rattle-rattle, rattle-rattle,
Bing.

*A deep rolling
bass.*

*More deliberate.
Solemnly chanted.*

*A rapidly piling
climax of speed
and racket.*

Boomlay, boomlay, boomlay, Boom,'
A roaring, epic, rag-time tune
From the mouth of the Congo
To the Mountains of the Moon.
Death is an Elephant,
Torch-eyed and horrible,
Foam-flanked and terrible.
Boom, steal the pygmies,
Boom, kill the Arabs,
Boom, kill the white men,
Hoo, Hoo, Hoo.
Listen to the yell of Leopold's ghost
Burning in Hell for his hand-maimed host.
Hear how the demons chuckle and yell
Cutting his hands off, down in Hell.
Listen to the creepy proclamation,
Blown through the lairs of the forest-nation,
Blown past the white-ants' hill of clay,
Blown past the marsh where the butterflies play:—
'Be careful what you do,
Or Mumbo-Jumbo, God of the Congo,
And all of the other
Gods of the Congo,
Mumbo-Jumbo will hoo-doo you,
Mumbo-Jumbo will hoo-doo you,
Mumbo-Jumbo will hoo-doo you.'

With a philosophic pause.

Shrilly and with a heavily accented metre.

Like the wind in the chimney.

All the O sounds very golden. Heavy accents very heavy. Light accents very light. Last line whispered.

II. *Their Irrepressible High Spirits*

Wild crap-shooters[1] with a whoop and a call
Danced the juba in their gambling-hall
And laughed fit to kill, and shook the town,
And guyed the policemen and laughed them down
With a boomlay, boomlay, boomlay, Boom.

Rather shrill and high.

[1] Gamblers with dice.

136

THEN I SAW THE CONGO, CREEPING THROUGH THE BLACK,

CUTTING THROUGH THE FOREST WITH A GOLDEN TRACK.

Read exactly as in first section.

A negro fairyland swung into view,
A minstrel river
Where dreams come true.
The ebony palace soared on high
Through the blossoming trees to the evening sky.
The inlaid porches and casements shone
With gold and ivory and elephant-bone.
And the black crowd laughed till their sides were sore
At the baboon butler in the agate door,
And the well-known tunes of the parrot band
That trilled on the bushes of that magic land.

Lay emphasis on the delicate ideas. Keep as light-footed as possible.

A troupe of skull-faced witch-men came
Through the agate doorway in suits of flame,
Yea, long-tailed coats with a gold-leaf crust
And hats that were covered with diamond-dust.
And the crowd in the court gave a whoop and a call
And danced the juba from wall to wall.
But the witch-men suddenly stilled the throng
With a stern cold glare, and a stern old song:—
'Mumbo-Jumbo will hoo-doo you.' . . .
Just then from the doorway, as fat as shotes,[1]
Came the cake-walk princes in their long red coats,
Canes with a brilliant lacquer shine,
And tall silk hats that were red as wine.

With pomposity.

With a great deliberation and ghostliness.

With over-whelming assurance, good cheer and pomp.

[1] Porkers.

And they pranced with their butterfly partners
    there,

With growing speed and sharply marked dance-rhythm.

Coal-black maidens with pearls in their hair,
Knee-skirts trimmed with the jassamine sweet,
And bells on their ankles and little black-feet.
And the couples railed at the chant and the frown
Of the witch-men lean, and laughed them down.
(O rare was the revel, and well worth while
That made those glowering witch-men smile.)
The cake-walk royalty then began
To walk for a cake that was tall as a man
To the tune of 'Boomlay, boomlay, Boom,'
While the witch-men laughed, with a sinister air,

With a touch of negro dialect, and as rapidly as possible toward the end.

And sang with the scalawags prancing there:—
'Walk with care, walk with care,
Or Mumbo-Jumbo, God of the Congo,
And all of the other
Gods of the Congo,
Mumbo-Jumbo will hoo-doo you.
Beware, beware, walk with care,
Boomlay, boomlay, boomlay, boom.
Boomlay, boomlay, boomlay, boom,
Boomlay, boomlay, boomlay, boom,
Boomlay, boomlay, boomlay,
Boom.'
Oh rare was the revel, and well worth while
That made those glowering witch-men smile.

Slow philosophic calm.

III. *The Hope of their Religion*

A good old negro in the slums of the town
Preached at a sister for her velvet gown.
Howled at a brother for his low-down ways,
His prowling, guzzling, sneak-thief days.
Beat on the Bible till he wore it out
Starting the jubilee revival shout.
And some had visions, as they stood on chairs,
And sang of Jacob, and the golden stairs,
And they all repented, a thousand strong
From their stupor and savagery and sin and wrong
And slammed with their hymn books till they
    shook the room
With 'glory, glory, glory,'
And 'Boom, boom, Boom.'

THEN I SAW THE CONGO, CREEPING THROUGH THE
    BLACK
CUTTING THROUGH THE JUNGLE WITH A GOLDEN
    TRACK.

And the gray sky opened like a new-rent veil
And showed the Apostles with their coats of mail.
In bright white steel they were seated round
And their fire-eyes watched where the Congo
    wound.
And the twelve Apostles, from their thrones on
    high
Thrilled all the forest with their heavenly cry:—

'Mumbo-Jumbo will die in the jungle;
Never again will he hoo-doo you,
Never again will he hoo-doo you.'
Then along that river, a thousand miles
The vine-snared trees fell down in files.

Side notes:

Heavy bass. With a literal imitation of camp-meeting racket, and trance.

Exactly as in the first section. Begin with terror and power, end with joy.

Sung to the tune of 'Hark, ten thousand harps and voices'.

With growing deliberation and joy.

139

Pioneer angels cleared the way
For a Congo paradise, for babes at play,
For sacred capitals, for temples clean.
Gone were the skull-faced witch-men lean.
There, where the wild ghost-gods had wailed In a rather high
A million boats of the angels sailed key—as delicately
With oars of silver, and prows of blue as possible.
And silken pennants that the sun shone through.
'Twas a land transfigured, 'twas a new creation.
Oh, a singing wind swept the negro nation
And on through the backwoods clearing flew:—
'Mumbo-Jumbo is dead in the jungle. To the tune of
Never again will he hoo-doo you. 'Hark, ten
Never again will he hoo-doo you.' thousand harps
  and voices'.

Redeemed were the forests, the beasts and the
    men,
And only the vulture dared again
By the far, lone mountains of the moon
To cry, in the silence, the Congo tune:—
'Mumbo-Jumbo will hoo-doo you,
Mumbo-Jumbo will hoo-doo you.
Mumbo ... Jumbo ... will ... hoo-doo ... Dying down
    you. into a pene-
  trating, terrified
  whisper.

                              VACHEL LINDSAY

VIII

The Revenge

A Ballad of the Fleet

I

AT Flores in the Azores Sir Richard Grenville lay,
And a pinnace, like a flutter'd bird, came flying from far away:
'Spanish ships of war at sea! we have sighted fifty-three!'
Then sware Lord Thomas Howard: ''Fore God I am no coward;
But I cannot meet them here, for my ships are out of gear,
And the half my men are sick. I must fly, but follow quick.
We are six ships of the line; can we fight with fifty-three?'

II

Then spake Sir Richard Grenville: 'I know you are no coward ;
You fly them for a moment to fight with them again.
But I've ninety men and more that are lying sick ashore.
I should count myself the coward if I left them, my Lord Howard,
To these Inquisition dogs and the devildoms of Spain.'

III

So Lord Howard past away with five ships of war that day,
Till he melted like a cloud in the silent summer heaven;
But Sir Richard bore in hand all his sick men from the land
Very carefully and slow,
Men of Bideford in Devon,
And we laid them on the ballast down below;
For we brought them all aboard,
And they blest him in their pain, that they were not left to
    Spain,
To the thumbscrew and the stake, for the glory of the Lord.

IV

He had only a hundred seamen to work the ship and to fight,
And he sailed away from Flores till the Spaniard came in sight,
With his huge sea-castles heaving upon the weather bow.
'Shall we fight or shall we fly?
Good Sir Richard, tell us now,
For to fight is but to die!
There'll be little of us left by the time this sun be set.'
And Sir Richard said again: 'We be all good English men.
Let us bang these dogs of Seville, the children of the devil,
For I never turn'd my back upon Don or devil yet.'

V

Sir Richard spoke and he laugh'd, and we roar'd a hurrah, and so
The little Revenge ran on sheer into the heart of the foe,
With her hundred fighters on deck, and her ninety sick below;
For half of their fleet to the right and half to the left were seen,
And the little Revenge ran on thro' the long sea-lane between.

VI

Thousands of their soldiers look'd down rom their decks and
    laugh'd,
Thousands of their seamen made mock at the mad little craft
Running on and on, till delay'd
By their mountain-like San Philip that, of fifteen hundred tons,
And up-shadowing high above us with her yawning tiers of guns,
Took the breath from our sails, and we stay'd.

VII

And while now the great San Philip hung above us like a cloud
Whence the thunderbolt will fall
Long and loud,
Four galleons drew away
From the Spanish fleet that day,
And two upon the larboard and two upon starboard lay,
And the battle-thunder broke from them all.

VIII

But anon the great San Philip, she bethought herself and went
Having that within her womb that had left her ill content;
And the rest they came aboard us, and they fought us hand to
hand,
For a dozen times they came with their pikes and musqueteers,
And a dozen times we shook 'em off as a dog that shakes his ears
When he leaps from the water to the land.

IX

And the sun went down, and the stars came out far over the
summer sea,
But never a moment ceased the fight of the one and the fifty-
three.
Ship after ship, the whole night long, their high-built galleons
came,

144

*steel
engraving by
A. Willmore
after
O. W. Brierly
published 1871*

Ship after ship, the whole night long, with her battle-thunder
    and flame;
Ship after ship, the whole night long, drew back with her dead
    and her shame.
For some were sunk and many were shatter'd, and so could fight
    us no more—
God of battles, was ever a battle like this in the world before?

X

For he said 'Fight on! fight on!'
Tho' his vessel was all but a wreck;
And it chanced that, when half of the short summer night was
    gone,
With a grisly wound to be drest he had left the deck,
But a bullet struck him that was dressing it suddenly dead,
And himself he was wounded again in the side of the head,
And he said 'Fight on! fight on!'

XI

And the night went down, and the sun smiled out far over the
    summer sea,
And the Spanish fleet with broken sides lay round us all in a ring;
But they dared not touch us again, for they fear'd that we still
    could sting,
So they watched what the end would be.
And we had not fought them in vain,
But in perilous plight were we,
Seeing forty of our poor hundred were slain,
And half of the rest of us maim'd for life
In the crash of the cannonades and the desperate strife;
And the sick men down in the hold were most of them stark and
    cold,
And the pikes were all broken or bent, and the powder was all
    of it spent;
And the masts and the rigging were lying over the side;
But Sir Richard cried in his English pride,
'We have fought such a fight for a day and a night
As may never be fought again!
We have won great glory, my men!
And a day less or more
At sea or ashore,
We die—does it matter when?
Sink me the ship, Master Gunner—sink her, split her in twain!
Fall into the hands of God, not into the hands of Spain!'

XII

And the gunner said, 'Ay, ay,' but the seamen made reply:
'We have children, we have wives,
And the Lord hath spared our lives.
We will make the Spaniard promise, if we yield, to let us go;

We shall live to fight again and to strike another blow.'
And the lion there lay dying, and they yielded to the foe.

XIII

And the stately Spanish men to their flagship bore him then,
Where they laid him by the mast, old Sir Richard caught at last,
And they praised him to his face with courtly foreign grace;
But he rose upon their decks, and he cried:
'I have fought for Queen and Faith like a valiant man and true;
I have only done my duty as a man is bound to do:
With a joyful spirit I Sir Richard Grenville die!'
And he fell upon their decks, and he died.

XIV

And they stared at the dead that had been so valiant and true,
And had holden the power and glory of Spain so cheap
That he dared her with one little ship and his English few;
Was he devil or man? He was devil for aught they knew,
But they sank his body with honour down into the deep,
And they mann'd the Revenge with a swarthier alien crew,
And away she sail'd with her loss and long'd for her own;
When a wind from the lands they had ruin'd awoke from sleep,
And the water began to heave and the weather to moan,
And or ever that evening ended a great gale blew,
And a wave like the wave that is raised by an earthquake grew,
Till it smote on their hulls and their sails and their masts and their
    flags,
And the whole sea plunged and fell on the shot-shatter'd navy of
    Spain,
And the little Revenge herself went down by the island crags
To be lost evermore in the main.

ALFRED LORD TENNYSON

147

INDEX OF TITLES AND FIRST LINES

Titles are given in italic type

148

INDEX OF AUTHORS

ACKNOWLEDGMENTS

THE EDITOR and publishers wish to thank the following for their permission to include copyright material in this anthology: Mrs Bambridge and Messrs Macmillan & Co Ltd for 'Puck's Song' from *Puck of Pook's Hill* by Rudyard Kipling; Messrs Constable & Co Ltd for 'Fighting South of the Castle' by Arthur Waley; Mrs Flecker for 'The Golden Journey to Samarkand' by J. E. Flecker; Mrs H. M. Davies and Messrs Jonathan Cape Ltd for 'A Child's Pet' from *The Collected Poems of W. H. Davies*; Messrs Jonathan Cape Ltd for 'The Beechwood' from *The Collected Poems of Andrew Young*; Dr John Masefield, O.M., and the Society of Authors for an extract from 'Right Royal'; the Literary Trustees of the late Walter de la Mare and Messrs Faber & Faber for 'Many a Mickle'; Miss Edith King and Messrs Basil Blackwell Ltd for 'Hope'; the Estate of the late Mrs Frieda Lawrence for 'Things Men Have Made' by D. H. Lawrence; the Trustees of the Hardy Estate and Messrs Macmillan & Co Ltd for 'The Old Workman' by Thomas Hardy; Mrs Stephens and Messrs Macmillan & Co Ltd for 'Seumas Beg' and 'To the Four Courts, please' from *Collected Poems* by James Stephens; the Macmillan Company, New York, for 'The Congo' by Vachel Lindsay; and the Oxford University Press for 'The Moonlit Stream' from *The Blackbird in the Lilac* by James Reeves. 'Queer Things' is taken from *The Wandering Moon* by James Reeves (Heinemann). The Authorised Version of the Holy Bible is Crown copyright, and the three extracts from it have been here printed by permission. Thanks are also due to the Trustees of the British Museum for the illustrations on pages 36, 98 and 126, to the Trustees of the National Maritime Museum, Greenwich, for the illustrations on pages 108 and 144–5.